Clinical Governance and the NHS Reforms: Enabling Excellence or Imposing Control

Titles of related interest in the UK Key Advances in Clinical Practice Series

NICE, CHI and the NHS Reforms: Enabling Excellence or Imposing Control

Clinical Governance and the NHS Reforms: Enabling Excellence or Imposing Control

Edited by

Andrew Miles MSc MPhil PhD
Professor of Public Health Policy, University of East London, London, UK

Alison P Hill BSc MBBS MSc MRCP FRCGP
Former Director of the Effectiveness Programme, King's Fund, London, UK

Brian Hurwitz MA MSc MD MRCGP FRCP
Professor of Primary Care and General Practice,
Imperial College of Science, Technology and Medicine, London, UK

UeL University Centre for Public Health Policy & Health Services Research

AESCULAPIUS MEDICAL PRESS
LONDON SAN FRANCISCO SYDNEY

Published by

Aesculapius Medical Press (London, San Francisco, Sydney)
Centre for Public Health Policy and Health Services Research
Faculty of Science and Health
University of East London
33 Shore Road, London E9 7TA, UK

First published 2001

British Library Cataloguing in Publication Data
A catalogue record for this book is available from the British Library

ISBN 1 903044 16 2

Further copies of this volume are available from:

Claudio Melchiorri
Research Dissemination Fellow
Centre for Public Health Policy and Health Services Research
Faculty of Science and Health
University of EastLondon
33 Shore Road, London E9 7TA, UK

Fax: 020 8525 8661
email: claudio@keyadvances4.demon.co.uk

Typeset, printed and bound in Britain
Peter Powell Origination & Print Limited

Contents

Contributors

Brian Ayers FRCR, Medical Director, Guy's and St Thomas' Hospital NHS Trust, London

Bruce G Charlton MD, Visiting Professor, UeL Centre for Public Health Policy and Health Services Research, London and Department of Psychology, University of Newcastle-upon-Tyne, Newcastle-upon-Tyne

Maureen Dalziel MBChB FFPHM, Director of NCC/SDO, London School of Hygiene and Tropical Medicine, London

Steve Dewar BA MA, King's Fund Fellow, King's Fund, London

Neville W Goodman MA DPhil FRCA, Consultant Anaesthetist, Southmead Hospital, Bristol

Aidan Halligan MB BCh BAO BA MA MD MRCPI MRCOG, Director of Clinical Governance for the NHS and Professor of Fetal and Maternal Medicine, University of Leicester

Shelley Heard MSc PhD FRCPath, Dean of Postgraduate Medicine, North Thames Department of Postgraduate and Medical and Dental Education, London

Phillipa Hewer BSc MSc DMS, Clinical Risk and Audit Manager, Whipps Cross University Hospital, London

Alison P Hill BSc MBBS MSc MRCP FRCGP, Formerly Director, Effectiveness Programme, King's Fund, London

Michael Loughlin PhD, Lecturer in Philosophy, Department of Humanities and Applied Social Studies, Manchester Metropolitan University, Manchester

Myriam Lugon MD FRCP, Formerly Medical Director, Whipps Cross University Hospital, London

Susanna Nicholls BA MB ChB, Researcher, NHS Clinical Governance Support Team, Leicester

Steve O'Neill BA MA FRSA, Deputy Head, Clinical Governance Support Team, Leicester

Carl Onion MSc MD MFPHM FRCGP, Medical Director, Wirral Health Authority, Tranmere, Birkenhead

Elisabeth Paice MA FRCP, Dean and Director of Postgraduate Medical and Dental Education, North Thames Department of Postgraduate and Medical and Dental Education, London

Preface

The advent of clinical governance as a major arm of health policy within the British NHS has been accompanied by much rhetoric but a relatively poor understanding of its core rationale with few studies designed with the aim of systematically examining its basic concept, its accompanying principle, and the methods by which it would be implemented, monitored, maintained and measured.

Rather than focus selectively on those aspects of clinical governance that are anticipated by its protagonists to provide measurable benefits to the NHS and which have been treated extensively elsewhere, the current volume preferentially addresses a range of areas of commonly expressed controversy and concern in relation to the impact of governance on clinical practice and service delivery in the immediate, medium and long term. Three different viewpoints emerge from the text: the view that clinical governance will deliver a sustained improvement in the quality of health services, the view that reserves judgement on this matter preferring a situation of 'watchful waiting' and the view that clinical governance is an essentially manipulative system born of an intuitively simple and basically naive political response to the substantial operational complexities of the British NHS, and that, as both a concept and a method, it will ultimately fail.

This sheer breadth and plurality of thought is perhaps honestly representative of currently prevailing opinion within the National Health Service and has the potential to contribute much to the development of the debate and to a mature understanding of the place of clinical governance in modern health care. We welcome such debate: it is in the nature of, and essential to, the proper process of science. It is in this spirit that we publish the set of eleven commentaries and viewpoints which form the present text and commend their use in the advancement of an open, balanced and intellectually rigorous debate.

Andrew Miles MSc MPhil PhD
Alison Hill BSc MBBS MSc MRCP FRCGP
Brian Hurwitz MA MSc MD MRCGP FRCP

Chapter 1

Clinical governance: philosophy, rhetoric and repression

Michael Loughlin

Introduction

Huge claims have been made on behalf of clinical governance. According to the Department of Health (1997) this 'central plank' of government policy will transform the health service, putting 'quality' at its 'heart'. Its adoption will 'assure and improve clinical standards' throughout the service by providing that 'good practice is rapidly disseminated and systems are in place to ensure constructive improvements in clinical care'.

Professor Liam Donaldson, the Chief Medical Officer and someone closely associated with the development of clinical governance in the UK, describes the document in which these claims are made as 'a watershed in the approach to quality in the NHS' (Donaldson 1999 p7) and states that:

> This is probably the most important development in the NHS for thirty years and will have profound implications for every hospital and primary care service as well as individual doctors and other health professionals.
>
> (*op. cit.*)

According to Donaldson:

> The introduction of clinical governance, aimed as it is at improving the quality of clinical care at all levels of healthcare provision, is by far the most ambitious quality initiative that will ever have been implemented in the NHS.
>
> (Scally & Donaldson 1998 p62)

What is apparently novel about this initiative is that it will not only 'maintain standards' but will also 'continuously improve quality' (*op. cit.*) by promoting 'accountability', 'the widespread adoption of the principles and methods of continuous quality improvement' (*ibid. p62*), 'excellence' and practice based on 'evidence' rather than 'opinion alone' (*ibid. p63*). Other enthusiasts for clinical governance describe it as 'a breathtaking idea, whose simplicity belies its complexity' (Hill 1999 p596) which will foster 'clinical effectiveness', 'the pursuit of excellence in clinical care' and 'the proper use of public money' (Morrison 1999 p163).

The confidence with which these claims are asserted might lead us to assume that a great deal of evidence exists to support them. This implies a more basic assumption still: that we all have a clear sense of what they *mean*, that we share a common understanding of what clinical governance is and its relationship with such things as 'quality', 'excellence', 'evidence' and the rest. (For it is not clear how I could go about finding the evidence to *verify* a claim if I did not know what that claim actually *meant*.) Indeed, Donaldson (1999 p9) implies that scepticism about the 'new era' that clinical governance promises to usher in betrays a 'cynical heart' – but he expresses the conviction that even a heart such as this should be 'melted' by a sufficiently eloquent evocation of the 'culture of excellence' which awaits us.

Yet in the same articles which make such grand claims, authors typically concede that no such common understanding exists. They could hardly fail to do so, for it is obvious. An article published recently in *Hospital Doctor* (Smy 1999) asked 25 'leading players in healthcare' what they thought the term meant and found, perhaps unsurprisingly, 'a degree of disparity in the way the term is used'. This is not because these 'leading players' have failed to do their research: it is not as if there is some 'correct' definition which they have simply neglected to learn. The White Paper which introduced the term omitted to define it, making the customary claims about its relationship to quality, excellence, improving standards and so forth without explaining how these terms or the criteria which justify their employment are to be understood. One of the defenders of the 'concept' of clinical governance suggests that 'many people outside the NHS' will be 'surprised' that no such thing exists already (Hill 1999 p596). I think that many more people would be surprised that vast sums of public money can be spent on implementing a policy which proposes to transform the practices of everyone in the health service, *before* anyone has taken the trouble to explain clearly what that policy means, or how its central claims are justified. This seems particularly incongruous when the key values the policy supposedly espouses include 'accountability' and the propagation of decisions based on 'sound evidence', to determine the 'effectiveness' of all decisions made and to guarantee that they represent a 'proper use of public money'.

The purpose of this chapter, then, is to examine some of the claims made on behalf of clinical governance by its most prominent defenders, in an attempt to discover their presuppositions and to see if they stand up to serious scrutiny. What are the 'principles and methods of continuous quality improvement' to which Donaldson and others refer? What conceptions of good practice and value in healthcare justify the claim that the 'widespread adoption' of these 'principles' will promote 'excellence' at 'all levels' of the service? What assumptions about the nature of knowledge, science and rationality are at work in the distinction between 'evidence' and 'opinion', underlying the conviction that clinical governance will champion the former by driving out the latter? Are these assumptions sustainable? In short, what are the conceptual foundations of clinical governance, and are they sound?

Vagueness and authoritarianism

I realise that these are not the sort of questions one is used to hearing in the discussion of health service policy, or of public policy more generally. Although the superlatives 'quality' and 'excellence' abound in government and management literature, it is not usually considered pertinent to ask for an explanation of their meaning, let alone a justification of their employment in defence of any specific policy decision.

To do so is to give away one's status as a 'philosopher' preoccupied with 'academic', and, by implication, frivolous concerns (Heginbotham 1994; Wall 1994 p317). It seems that those who exercise power in our contemporary democracies, or who hope in some way to influence the policy-making process, have come to a similar conclusion to the one reached by their predecessors in ancient Athenian democracy. That is, that critical reflection upon the meanings of terms has no place in the discussion of any matter of practical importance, and those who subject fundamental assumptions to rigorous intellectual questioning have no business in bothering serious persons with their 'intellectual ruminations' (Wall *op. cit.*). Fortunately it is no longer deemed necessary to deal with such academic irritants by requiring them to drink hemlock. It is considered more humane, and certainly more economical, to respond with derision, or to ignore them altogether (Loughlin M 1994b p310).

It is fair to say that the questions raised above are philosophical in nature, in the following sense: they are not technical questions about how to *implement* the policy under discussion, but rather they concern fundamental *conceptual* issues about what the policy assumes and what grounds (if any) we have been given to accept those assumptions. Until we can answer these questions we really have no way of knowing why we should think it a good policy in the first place, and so we cannot know whether or not we should *want* to see it implemented. What I find disturbing is the idea that it is somehow impertinent, frivolous or eccentric to expect policy-makers to know what they are talking about, to be capable of reflecting critically upon their own assumptions and to be prepared to explain and defend them to the rest of us. For this suggests that those of us who are affected by the policy (all who practise in, and indeed all who may need to use the service) should concern ourselves simply with questions of implementation. It implies *either* that foundational questions (about 'why' as opposed to 'how' to implement the policy) are none of our business, that we should leave such matters to 'the great and the good', *or* that their answers are so obvious that it is a waste of time even bothering to state them.

The view that one's own assumptions are too obvious to merit serious debate is the hallmark of an ideologue, and I have argued previously that this mentality is not so much pragmatic as dogmatic and authoritarian (Loughlin M 2000 p3). All thinking requires the employment of theories, and no theory with substantial implications for practice is self-evident. Even my beliefs about where I am and what I am doing right now only make sense against the background of a complex system of beliefs that I have built up throughout the course of my life, and that I will continue updating and revising for as long as my brain still functions. Different theories represent different ways in which beliefs and experience can be organised. They are the conceptual maps which we need to negotiate our world. Strip away the theoretical backdrop – wipe clean the intellectual slate – and one has not the basis for coherent practical thinking but disorganised experiences, robbed of all meaning and practical significance. So the choice for a practically-minded person is not whether or not to employ theories but which theories to employ, and if I am at all reflective I will realise that I may have gone wrong in my thinking at some point along the way. Even some of my most basic assumptions may be contentious, meaning that they are not necessarily shared by every other rational person. It is therefore surely a feature of any intelligent approach to practice that one remains aware of one's own fallibility, keeping all assumptions in principle open to revision.

These points become clearer when we consider judgements about important and controversial matters of public policy. Frequently, disagreements about which policy is 'right' are not based in some straightforward difference of opinion, easily settled by appeal to certain facts whose nature all parties to the dispute recognise. Rather they can be traced to fundamental differences about such matters as the proper goal of social policy, the nature and extent of our obligations to other members of the community, or the relationship between (and respective values of) individual liberties and social cohesion. Unless these basic assumptions are brought to the fore and examined in detail, debates will typically be confused and participants will appear to be arguing at cross purposes (Loughlin A 1998 pp62–66).

We can all, for instance, agree that a policy should be 'fair' to all affected parties, but if that verbal agreement disguises radically different beliefs about what fairness eally means then we have no substantial agreement about anything. Unless we are willing to explore, with clarity and intellectual honesty, our different conceptions of fairness, we will not even come to understand the nature of our differences, let alone come any closer to resolving them. Public debate becomes not a dialogue between free and rational persons with the shared goal of discovering the truth, but a verbal battlefield, where parties compete for ownership of persuasive terminology. Hence the constant repetition of the terms 'equity', 'autonomy', 'empowerment', 'effectiveness', 'efficiency', 'respecting rights', 'meeting needs' and of course 'excellence' and 'quality' in government and management literature, accompanied by a stubborn refusal to analyse these terms and, indeed, an expressed disdain for those who maintain that they *need* any analysis. For to admit this would be to allow that their appropriation and employment in defence of one's chosen policies was a contentious exercise, requiring detailed argument in its defence. (Insofar as these terms are 'analysed' the analysis is circular and superficial: authors might claim to have 'discovered' certain 'aspects' or 'dimensions' of 'quality', and these will turn out to be such things as 'effectiveness' and 'equity'. Then, without much further ado, all of these things are declared to be the anticipated 'outcomes' or 'products' of the policies being 'defended'.)

In such a poor intellectual climate, arguments are 'settled' by appeal to bald rhetoric, and whichever side has the catchiest slogans will be deemed to have 'won the day'. We do not need to search very far for examples of this style of debate: tune into any debate in the House of Commons, watch an episode of *Question Time* on BBC television or attend any public forum where political ideologues display their skills in verbal jousting, and you will be rewarded with the approving grunts of their supporters. Indeed, so natural is this picture to those of us brought up in a liberal political culture that it may seem simply to characterise the essence of practical debate, such that the shocking stupidity of a society which makes all its most serious decisions in this way rarely seems to trouble us (Loughlin M 1995a p37).

Stupidity in public debate breeds authoritarianism in politics. The refusal to waste time discussing 'ideas' functions to protect from critical scrutiny the set of ideas behind the most fashionable or dominant approaches to practice, such that possibilities are only deemed 'practical' if they are compatible with the ruling dogmas of the day (Loughlin M 2000 p3). Increasingly, 'explaining' a policy means enunciating certain general principles and all the interesting questions – about how that policy is to be interpreted and applied within specific contexts – are left deliberately unclear. In that case the substantial meaning of the policy will be determined by those (in government and senior management) who are empowered to interpret it, while it will be justified (to the workforce and the population at large) with reference to all the persuasive rhetorical force of the formal principle: to say one opposes it will be to say one is opposed to 'equity' and all the good things the policy has been officially deemed to represent. Thus a climate is created in which it appears unreasonable, reactionary or eccentric to oppose the dominant ethos, whatever it may be. Where philosophy is derided, language becomes not a tool to facilitate critical thinking and communication, but a blunt instrument to 'deliver support' for policies (in the words of one senior manager) (Spiers 1994 p189) or (in my words) it becomes 'another stick in the already impressive armoury of the powerful' (Loughlin M 1994a p47).

To fail to think critically about one's fundamental assumptions is to allow one's ideas and attitudes, and ultimately one's behaviour, to be shaped by forces that one fails to understand, let alone control (Loughlin M 2000 p5). We need to acquire the habit of sustained critical thinking. We need to learn how to ask irritating questions. The alternative is to become 'opinion-fodder' for political spin-doctors and workplace ideologues to experiment upon with impunity. And if that is our fate then our minds are in a very real sense not our own.

Examining the conceptual foundations

We are therefore in no position to assess for ourselves the impressive claims made on behalf of clinical governance, until we understand the specific set of assumptions which underlie them. It would be not so much 'cynical' as wilfully perverse to question the desirability of a new era of quality, in which excellent practices, accountability and the effective use of evidence abound. However, it seems to me that scepticism about clinical governance may indicate not the moral flaw of cynicism, nor any problem with one's 'heart', but that it may instead be symptomatic of nothing more worrying than a well functioning brain, and the propensity for clear thinking and intellectual honesty.

Scally and Donaldson (1998 p62) define clinical governance in the following terms:

> Clinical governance is a system through which NHS organisations are accountable for continuously improving the quality of their services and safeguarding high standards of care by creating an environment in which excellence in clinical care will flourish.

Evidently this definition is only informative if we have some idea of what they mean by 'quality' and how they think it can be 'continuously improved'. What sort of 'system' is being envisaged to make possible such perpetual improvement? What is 'clinical excellence' and what type of environment will make it 'flourish'?

Fortunately the article which proffers this definition gives us something to go on. In particular, there are three features of the account which strike me as significant. These are:

1. A view about what 'good evidence' means, underlying a specific conception of good clinical practice.
2. The organisational structure envisaged to promote this conception of good practice.
3. A 'quality improvement philosophy' derived from contemporary 'management science'.

The authors state that, thanks to the 'evidence-based medicine movement', it is increasingly the case that 'neither clinical decisions nor health policy can any longer comfortably be based on opinion alone' (*ibid.* p63). Under the heading 'Evidence and good practice' they claim that clinical governance will support the latter by promoting the use of the former: good practice, it seems, means 'evidence based practice' (*op. cit.*).

The claim that medical practice should be based on evidence is rather like the claims that policies should be fair to all affected parties, that economic arrangements should be equitable and that services should display quality. That is to say, as a purely formal claim it is platitudinous: no-one could seriously defend the view that ignorant, opinionated practitioners are better than well informed ones. The really interesting questions concern how this formal claim is to be interpreted in practice: what is meant by 'evidence' and how, in the first place, do we identify good evidence and distinguish it from bad evidence? In particular, given the contentious nature of so many issues in medical research and medical practice, can any one person or group claim an epistemologically privileged perspective that would allow them to define, authoritatively, what 'good evidence' does and does not mean?

Unfortunately, the 'movement' to which Scally and Donaldson refer so approvingly applies the method of argument I have just been criticising as dogmatic and authoritarian. That is to say, its exponents take the persuasive, rhetorical force of the formal claim and supply, with little or no argument, their own substantial account of the meaning of 'evidence', defining the term stipulatively as applying only to certain very specific sources of evidence. Then, any practitioner who wishes to appeal to sources of evidence not approved by the movement is, by definition, a bad practitioner. So the word 'evidence' (with all its rhetorical force) has effectively been claimed as the exclusive property of those who take a particular (and controversial) view of what good evidence means. In the absence of widespread agreement amongst colleagues about the nature of evidence this movement is rightly condemned as 'arrogant' (Polychronis *et al.* 1996b p10). I think we can go further than this. Without a detailed explanation and defence of the conceptions of knowledge, science and practical reasoning which underlie this specific view of good evidence, the attempt to restrict the term's application in this way is arbitrary and irrational.

The contrast between 'evidence' and 'opinion' implies we have some clear line of demarcation between the two. Its use in this context suggests that evidence derived from clinical research can, in some fairly straightforward and uncontroversial way, be directly applied to practice, without the need for subjective judgement and without the need to take account of context-specific information which may affect one's decision one way or another. But why should such 'subjective' and contextual information be dismissed as somehow not proper knowledge or as 'unscientific'? It is quite extraordinary that a movement dedicated to basing conclusions on up-to-date research, can ground its own views about the nature of science in a positivistic theory of science that has been refuted for decades. All credible positions in the philosophy of science (and this includes positions as different as those of Popper (1989) and Feyerabend (1988)) accept the following points:

1. Observation is a theory-laden exercise. As noted above, without a theoretical backdrop the data of experience are robbed of all meaning and practical significance.
2. The under-determination of theory by data (Quine 1969). In all the most interesting and important areas of science the available data do not determine, deductively, any one theoretical position as *evidently* correct, therefore.
3. Subjective judgements about the selection of the data to form the basis for conclusions are ineliminable. Individual judgement is not infallible, but nor can we do without it: to condemn it as 'subjective' in some reprehensible sense is to make scientific reasoning impossible (Loughlin AJ 1998 p95–121).

Of course, there are some examples of practice which are just plain bad, where practitioners have ignored what, on any intuitively acceptable account of the term, was important evidence. It is by no means clear that we can eliminate such bad practice by denying the theoretical and highly contentious nature of science or the need for the exercise of sound judgement. Nor is it immediately obvious that the price we would have to pay would be acceptable. Since, on any defensible theory of 'good science' and on any plausible account of 'good practice', the exercise of sound critical judgement is essential, any approach which causes us to ignore or undervalue the role of critical judgement is likely to impoverish rather than improve practices. What we need, then, is to give more attention to the question of how to develop the skill and encourage the exercise of independent, critical thinking. A good environment means, minimally, one which fosters the development of this skill and facilitates its exercise. By parity of reasoning, an environment is bad to the extent that it inhibits or prohibits this.

This brings us to the second of the points above, concerning the organisational structure. *If* the assumptions about evidence just examined were correct, then it might make sense to disseminate good practice throughout the service firstly, by establishing an authoritative source of guidelines for practitioners on such matters as the effectiveness and efficiency of treatment options, then secondly by putting in place mechanisms to ensure that these guidelines are being implemented throughout the service. This way it would become 'standard practice' for all decisions to be based upon the 'best evidence' available. Scally and Donaldson (1998) note (p63) the creation of two new institutions – the National Institute for Clinical Excellence (NICE) and the Commission for Health Improvement (CHI). According to its chairman, NICE will evelop sets of clinical guidelines representing 'a single, authoritative source of advice' to health professionals and their managers on the clinical and cost-effectiveness of any decisions about treatment (Rawlins 1999 p1079). The role of CHI, it appears, will be to monitor the implementation of these guidelines.

The trouble is, the assumptions about evidence are questionable. In the absence of any one authoritative view of what constitutes 'best evidence', it is surely arbitrary to impose one particular set of judgements upon an entire working population. Given that a diversity of reasonable approaches to many health problems is left open by the sum total of human knowledge to date, it seems rational to allow a plurality of approaches in the solution of those problems (Loughlin M 2000 p11). An environment of honest debate and disagreement is more likely to give rise to scientific progress than one based upon the false claim that there is a single source of authoritative judgements (Charlton 1993 p100). Given the heterogeneous nature of patients, it is also more likely to allow for treatments appropriate to the needs of specific patients – something which is surely a feature of 'good practice' in any defensible sense.

Regrettably we live in an age obsessed with the production of regulatory frameworks, sets of guidelines, codes of practice and the like. It is generally assumed that spending massive amounts of money on producing such frameworks, and then checking that everyone is following them (requiring in practice the constant monitoring of people's behaviour) is the best way to improve practices in healthcare, education and elsewhere. (It is worth noting that it is by no means clear what the 'evidence' is for this assumption.) Although lip-service is sometimes paid to the idea of the 'reflective practitioner', and Scally & Donaldson (1998 p65) refer to the need to encourage staff to 'participate' in looking 'critically' at existing practices, the obvious danger in this approach to improving practice is that the use of critical individual judgement is increasingly discouraged. Thus, the chairman of NICE warns that 'health professionals would be wise to record their reasons for non-compliance' with NICE guidelines in patients' medical records since such 'non-compliance' may precipitate an investigation by CHI (Rawlins 1999).

By fiat the professional world is being divided into the makers and the followers of rules. Whatever the rhetoric employed, this structural division promotes a conception of 'good practice' which is the antithesis of critical thinking: i.e., a 'good' practitioner is one who 'knows the rules' in her area and follows them, whatever they are. 'I was only following procedure' becomes an automatic defence: even if the outcome was disastrous, and even if one feels that a properly trained practitioner should have known instinctively that in this case it would be disastrous, the practitioner was formally 'correct' to follow the guidelines. Contextual knowledge, the implicit, the unquantifiable (Polychronis *et al.* 1996a p2) and the personal[1] are equally devalued, as practitioners are encouraged to ignore any considerations which cannot easily be justified to someone charged to monitor the implementation of practice guidelines – someone who is necessarily operating at a distance from the immediate context in which the decision was made. Until an account of practical reasoning has been offered to explain why such considerations are not relevant, it would seem that this approach encourages practitioners to ignore practically relevant considerations arbitrarily (without argument). It therefore promotes irrationality in practice.

Further, the 'guidelines' approach to improving practice has all the dangers of encouraging authoritarianism noted above. Decisions about clinical effectiveness require individual judgement, including value judgements. (The same is true about 'cost effectiveness', whose evaluative component becomes apparent once this concept is properly analysed: a point I make in Loughlin M 2000 pp9–10). Guidelines must always be general in nature, so there will always be a gap between the formal guideline and its interpretation and appropriate application in any given situation. Since guidelines are only meaningful if they may be enforced, in reality this gap will be bridged by the judgements of those with the power to enforce the guidelines. Thus complex intellectual and evaluative questions may be settled by the exercise of political power.

---

1 In the new, evidence-based, consumer-focused professional world under construction, terms like 'instinct' and 'personal experience' are too often sneered at, dismissed with labels like 'subjective' and 'anecdotal', when they are clearly basic components of common sense and practical rationality in the real world. (Another term typically used rhetorically: I mean it simply to refer to our shared experience of day to day existence that defines our common humanity.)

Evidence-based management?

So it is that an intellectually restrictive conception of evidence leads logically to a simplistic view of good practice, and this translates into a political prescription for restricting and controlling the behaviour of practitioners. The mechanisms of control therefore become the key tools for the promotion of quality, so it is hardly surprising that the authors feel attracted to a 'quality improvement philosophy' which treats the quality of an organisation as a function of its management structure (Scally & Donaldson 1998 p62).

Immediately following the claim about promoting the 'widespread adoption of the principles and methods of continuous quality improvement', Scally & Donaldson (1998) explain that these 'principles' were 'developed in the industrial sector and then later applied to healthcare'*(op. cit.)*. They cite with approval an article by Berwick (1989) which calls for the introduction of 'quality management science' into the health service, claiming that the importation of principles derived from the world of commerce into health practice will automatically, 'scientifically' and 'continuously' 'raise the quality curve' of the service. Berwick maintains that commercially-trained 'quality engineers' should 'occupy a central place' in any organisational structure, 'training' all members of staff to construe their various activities as part of a corporate 'production process', since 'all staff members must become partners in the central mission of quality improvement'. Given these influences, it comes as no surprise that the term 'clinical governance' is 'derived from the commercial world' (Hill 1999 p596), specifically the idea of 'corporate governance' in business (Scally & Donaldson 1998 p61).

I have argued extensively elsewhere (Loughlin M 1993a, 1994a and b, 1995b, 1996) that the attempt to evaluate practices in healthcare in terms of a language and conceptual framework developed to characterise practices in commercial sector is fundamentally misguided. 'Health' and 'education' are not 'products' in the same sense as the standard lamps and Xerox machines of Berwick's illustrations, and the translation of such terms as 'patient' and 'student' into 'consumer' or 'customer' begs a number of foundational questions. While the term 'quality' retains its rhetorical force in any context, its substantial meaning changes depending on the purposes of the activity being evaluated (Loughlin M 1995b p83). So this management 'science' has no solid conceptual base. Its 'theorists' speak of 'basic organisational criteria' (Loughlin M 1994b pp137–138) which they claim can be applied to any complex organisation, but when they attempt to spell out these criteria they are incapable of explaining them in any detail, resorting instead to the mantra-like repetition of persuasive rhetoric.

Because the 'science' is founded upon the rhetorical force of certain words, it is possible for authors to declare a term foundational to their branch of the science, then to go on to admit that they have not yet thought what the term might mean. Two defenders of the application of Total Quality Management (TQM) and

Continuous Quality Improvement (CQI) approaches to quality in the NHS admit that the 'quest' for 'total quality' is made 'more testing' by the fact that no-one knows how to define quality, and as a consequence their favoured approaches had to be 'launched' and 'operationalised' before they were 'fully conceptualised' (Joss & Kogan 1995 pp5 and 43, criticised in Loughlin M 1996). Scores of articles describing the application of TQM to some particular part of the NHS take the following form:

1. Senior management in a health authority becomes 'converted' and 'totally committed' to TQM (usually on the basis of nothing more tangible than the heartfelt 'conviction' of a senior figure that 'quality matters' (Jones & Macilwaine 1991)).
2. Management and staff are required to invest time and money in implementing the approach, setting up quality structures, senior management steering groups, monitoring procedures, appointing full or part time quality co-ordinators, and so on.
3. Management calls for a series of workshops to 'investigate' what quality management means (Loughlin M 1993a).

Similarly the term 'health gain' enjoyed brief popularity in the early 1990s, after certain 'experts' in the field of health services management announced that the purpose of the health service was not simply to make people healthier, but rather, its goal was to produce 'health gains'. As far as I can tell, the only advantage of this term was that it sounded like a 'product': talk of producing health gains sounds more like an industrial production process than 'making people better', 'treating illnesses' and the like. On this rather flimsy intellectual basis the term was declared to be the 'new buzzword of the nineties' (Liddle 1992a p1) and its discovery was heralded as a massive conceptual advance. Two 'standing conferences' were held in its honour (funded, of course, with public money) and scores of publications and other circulated documents explored the nuances of this new 'technical term', which was declared to be 'a radical and challenging concept' (Chambers 1992 p11), the 'way forward' for the service (Eskin 1992) and even the 'philosophical basis' for, and 'the ultimate purpose of the NHS' (Liddle 1992a *op. cit.*). Yet in the same articles in which such claims were made (often in the same paragraphs) authors admitted that they could not say what health gains were and that no known method existed to define or measure them. 'Research' into the concept typically took the form of highly-paid administrators writing to their colleagues in other parts of the country asking them what they felt the term 'meant to them' and collating any responses received. Unsurprisingly, answers received usually made reference to the idea that 'producing health gains' had something to do with making people healthier, although it also had a lot to do with 'empowering' people, 'developing' them and so forth. Some of these pieces of 'research' are described in Loughlin M (1993b).

Perhaps it will come as no great shock to the reader that the activity of translating the language of 'making people healthier' into talk of 'producing health gains' did not, in fact, produce any 'measurable benefits' to the 'consumers' of healthcare. It is also unsurprising (although nonetheless shocking) that no-one ever undertook a study of the 'efficiency' of devoting large sums of public money to the project of 'empowering' senior administrators and so-called management theorists quite literally to 'investigate' the meaning of their own jargon. At a time when people with valuable practical and intellectual skills were being made redundant, and patients were being told that the resources to meet their needs were simply not available, how could it seem 'rational' to so many, to waste so much money in the name of 'efficiency'? How could anyone think that one can go on a quest for something, co-ordinate it, implement it, operationalise it, but not know what it is? How did they know what to look for? How did they expect to recognise it if ever they found it?

It is hard to imagine any other science where this would be acceptable. It is more usual in scientific practice for intellectual work to precede the invention of terminology. Phenomena are discovered and concepts developed, and a language is formulated to accommodate these discoveries and developments. In 'management science', the invention of terminology precedes intellectual work (Loughlin M 1994b p138). Terms or phrases are coined, then work begins to 'give' them some meaning. The widespread application of this 'science' in the health service has engendered what might be described as the 'buzzword approach to policy formation'. Pick a word, either because it sounds good or because it (or something very like it) is already being employed extensively in industry, then try to encourage its widespread use in the health service. At some point declare that it has become a 'key concept' and perhaps even the 'philosophical basis' for health service activities (Liddle 1992a *op. cit.*), a 'cornerstone' (Brooks 1992 p18) or indeed a 'major cornerstone' (Al-Assaf & Schmele 1993 p3) of healthcare.

Clearly we have grounds to question the rationality of this methodology. Would clinicians be encouraged to practise in this way? Would this count as an 'evidence-based' approach? How different are things today? Compare and contrast the following quotations:

> … it is a pity to condemn such a potentially useful term without a serious attempt to give it some consistent meaning
>
> (Liddle 1992b, writing about 'health gain')

> Only one thing is absolutely clear about clinical governance – that it's arrived. But what does it really mean?
>
> (Smy 1999)

Something has arrived, but what exactly? If one doesn't know what a term means one cannot know that it denotes something useful. 'Clinical governance' is a current buzzword, but will it prove any more useful than the buzzwords of the past? Donaldson's affection for management theory, which has been at work in most of the management reforms we have seen in the health service since the 1980s, raises the question: to what extent are these latest reforms really a radical break with the past (a 'watershed', as he puts it) as opposed merely to being the logical conclusion of a movement towards increased managerial control of practices which has been gaining momentum for two decades?

There is a further pertinent question: what is the likely effect on workers in the service of this culture of perpetual change – engendered, it would appear, by the predilection for linguistic innovation which characterises current management strategies in the health service? Is the introduction of yet another management reform really likely to improve morale, to 'inspire and enthuse' (Scally & Donaldson 1998 p65)? Some years ago Darbyshire (1993) described a sense of 'alienation' and 'despair' as he watched the service being transformed into 'an ideologue's adventure playground'. It is of course always possible that Donaldon's inspirational rhetoric will 'melt his heart', but I hope and believe that it will require something rather more substantial than this to convince a quite properly critical working populace of the benefits of this latest management innovation.

Conclusion

Governance, without a rationale that is clear and intelligible to those being governed, is repression, and as rational beings we have not only the 'right' but the duty to resist this. In the absence of a much more rigorous, intellectually credible explanation and defence of the policy than anything that has been produced so far, practitioners and the public at large should be extremely sceptical about the alleged advantages of 'clinical governance'. To confuse this quite proper intellectual expression of scepticism with 'cynicism' is to employ a deeply manipulative rhetorical device. The refusal to be swept along by unexplained rhetoric is not a sign of a defective heart, but rather it shows that one's heart and brain are still in full working order. When well-educated persons employ such rhetorical devices, one cannot avoid the conclusion that it is they who are being 'cynical' – and then one wonders what agendas lie behind the smokescreen of inspirational language, and the plethora of flow diagrams, pictures of temples and the like that are offered in place of any clear account of the true substance of what is being proposed. If to wonder about this is to have become infected with cynicism, then let us be clear about the source of the infection. Philosophy has been compared with a 'knife' (Pirsig 1988 p77) and a method of 'intellectual and moral self-defence' (Loughlin M 2000 p5). Like it or not, we need to cut through the nonsense and to examine directly whatever lies behind it, if our hearts and minds are to survive the corrupting influences of our age.

References

Al-Assaf AF & Schmele JA (1993). *The Textbook of Total Quality in Healthcare.* Florida: St Lucie Press

Berwick DM (1989). Continuous improvement as an ideal in healthcare. *New England Journal of Medicine* **320**, 53–56

Brooks T (1992). Total quality management in the NHS. *Health Services Management* **18**, 17–19

Chambers J (1992). Health gain – is there a need for the centre?' *HFA News 2000* **19**, 10–12

Charlton B (1993). Management of science. *The Lancet* **342**, 99–100

Darbyshire P (1993). Preserving nursing care in a destitute time. *Journal of Advanced Nursing* **18**, 507–508

Department of Health (1997). *The New NHS – Modern, Dependable*. London: HMSO

Donaldson L (1999). Clinical governance – medical practice in a new era. *The Journal of The MDU* **15**, 7–9

Eskin F (1992). Developing public health practitioners for health gain: what needs to be different?' *HFA News 2000* **19**, 2–5

Feyerabend P (1988). *Against Method.* London: Verso Books

Heginbotham C (1994). Management worries. Letter to the editor. *Healthcare Analysis* **2**, 270

Hill P (1999). Clinical governance – an educational perspective. *Hospital Medicine* **60**, 596–598

Jones T & Macilwaine H (1991). Diagnosing the organisation: one health authority's experience of total quality management. *International Journal of Healthcare Quality Assurance* **4**, 21–24

Joss R & Kogan M (1995). *Advancing Quality: Total Quality Management in the National Health Service.* Buckingham: Open University Press

Liddle A (1992a). *Health Gain.* Norwich: Health Gain 92. Proceedings from The Standing Conference

Liddle A (1992b). Why should general managers be involved with health gain? *HFA 2000 News* **19**, 13–15

Loughlin AJ (1998). *Alienation and Value-Neutrality*. Aldershot: Ashgate Publishing Ltd

Loughlin M (1993a). The illusion of quality. *Healthcare Analysis* **1**, 69–73

Loughlin M (1993b). The strange quest for the health gain. *Healthcare Analysis* **1**, 165–169

Loughlin M (1994a). Behind the wall paper. *Healthcare Analysis* **2**, 47–53

Loughlin M (1994b). The poverty of management. *Healthcare Analysis* **2**, 135–139

Loughlin M (1994c). The silence of philosophy. *Healthcare Analysis* **2**, 310–316

Loughlin M (1995a). Dworkin, Rawls and reality. *Healthcare Analysis* **3**, 37–43

Loughlin M (1995b). Brief encounter: a dialogue between a philosopher and an NHS manager on the subject of "quality". *Journal of Evaluation in Clinical Practice* **1**, 81–85

Loughlin M (1996). The language of quality. *Journal of Evaluation in Clinical Practice* **2**, 87–95

Loughlin M (2000). Quality and excellence: meaning versus rhetoric. In *NICE, CHI and the NHS Reforms.*Miles A, Hampton JR, Hurwitz B (eds). London: Aesculapius Medical Press pp1–12

Miles A, Hampton JR, Hurwitz B (2000). *NICE, CHI and the NHS Reforms.* London: Aesculapius Medical Press

Morrison J (1999). Clinical governance – implications for medical education. *Medical Education* **33**, 162–164

Pirsig RM (1988). *Zen and the Art of Motorcycle Maintenance*. London: Transworld Publishers

Polychronis A, Miles A, Bentley P (1996a). Evidence-based medicine: reference? dogma? neologism? new orthodoxy? *Journal of Evaluation in Clinical Practice* **2**, 1–3

Polychronis A, Miles A, Bentley P (1996b). The protagonists of “evidence-based medicine”: arrogant, seductive and controversial. *Journal of Evaluation in Clinical Practice* **2**, 9–12

Popper K (1989). *Objective Knowledge: an Evolutionary Approach*. Oxford: Clarendon Press

Quine WVO (1969). Epistemology naturalised. In *Ontological Relativity and Other Essays*. New York: Columbia University Press. pp 69–90

Rawlins M (1999). In pursuit of quality: the National Institute for Clinical Excellence. *The Lancet* **353**, 1079–1082

Scally G & Donaldson L (1998). Clinical governance and the drive for quality improvement in the new NHS in England. *British Medical Journal* **317**, 61–65

Smy J (1999). So what does clinical governance mean? *Hospital Doctor* **April 1999**, 30

Spiers J (1994). Extract from: ‘Whose side are you on anyway? Sharpening purchaser leadership – a patient-focused trust perspective. *Healthcare Analysis* **2**, 187–190

Wall A (1994). Behind the wallpaper: a rejoinder. *Healthcare Analysis* **2**, 317–318

Chapter 2

Clinical governance: aligning accountabilities

Steve Dewar

Introduction

Putting clinical governance into place means changing the way healthcare accountabilities are enacted, monitored and built into the healthcare system. Changing accountability arrangements goes to the heart of how individuals relate to each other and the organisation that they work within, as well as how these organisations relate to other organisations in the wider healthcare system. Understanding the relationship between clinical governance and accountability arrangements helps explain why implementing clinical governance is such a difficult political and cultural challenge.

The purpose of this chapter is threefold. First, to examine the relationship between clinical governance and new arrangements for holding the individuals and the organisations that deliver healthcare to account. Secondly, to specifically test the strength and clarity of two new proposed areas of accountability, the *Statutory Duty of Quality* (Stationery Office 1999), and the proposals for more modern systems of professional regulation contained in *Assuring the Quality of Medical Practice and Supporting Doctors: Protecting Patients* (Department of Health 1999, 2000). Thirdly, and in conclusion, to address the question of whether clinical governance is a system for enabling healthcare systems to develop excellent services or a mechanism for imposing greater control over healthcare professionals.

Clinical governance and accountability cannot be divorced – achieving and demonstrating improvement are two sides of the same coin. But to assure the effective assurance of quality (clinical governance) requires clarity over who holds healthcare professionals and organisations to account and how this is done. However, accountabilities for healthcare professionals are complex and potentially contradictory and the way in which these accountabilities are jointly understood, enacted, and scrutinised remains unclear.

The *Statutory Duty of Quality* (Stationery Office 1999) changes the climate of accountability for chief executives of trusts but is still far from clear if chief executives will be held responsible for identifying or acting on concerns over clinical quality. The proposals in *Assuring the Quality of Medical Practice* and its parent consultation paper *Supporting Doctors: Protecting Patients* represent a radical set of new arrangements that legitimise action by peers and employers when faced with possible poor clinical performance. However, when tested many key questions about these proposals would remain unanswered. Of course the detail is always to be worked through. However, if clinical governance depends on clear lines of accountability then questions of respective roles and responsibilities need to be addressed urgently.

Clinical governace may deliver both improving quality of care and greater control over healthcare professionals. But real accountability lies not in the complexities of policy and procedure for GP practice, hospital trust, the Commision for Health Improvement, the new National Clinical Assessment Authority or a reformed GMC but in the shared expectations that might best guide the often private interaction between patient and healthcare professional.

The relationship between clinical governance and arrangements for accountability

There are three ways of understanding the relationship between implementing clinical governance and establishing new arrangements for accountability:

1. Establishing new accountabilities is one way of trying to 'drive' or performance manage the delivery of this new approach to quality. Arrangements for accountability are the means, effective clinical governance the ends.
2. Alternatively clinical governance is the means and effective accountability for clinicians (particularly doctors) the ends.
3. Or both options might be simplistic given that clinical governance is itself a framework of accountability (for quality) and effectively intertwines the concepts so as to make them almost synonymous.

Accountability: a means to achieving clinical governance

> Successful clinical governance will rely on proper arrangements for accountability, which are seen to be effective by the public.
>
> (Department of Health 1998)

Here, successful clinical governance is presented as the desirable 'end', 'proper arrangements for accountability' as the 'means', with the public as arbitrator of effectiveness.

If 'proper' accountability arrangements provide the road that leads to effective clinical governance then what are these arrangements and what makes them 'proper'? At an organisational level this dilemma is crystallised in the different models that are currently being tried for making individuals, teams and directorates accountable without damaging the ownership and participation that are crucial parts of an environment that fosters quality improvement. At a wider level, regional offices and the Commission for Health Improvement (CHI) must question how they can manage accountability for delivering increasing numbers of national targets while recognising the need for 'bottom-up' priorities also to emerge and drive the process of change.

Clinical governance: a means to greater accountability

> Clinical governance means the standards by which clinical practice is demonstrated and judged. The most important aspect is to link health service management with the process of continuous self-regulation of the medical profession. If we can bring those two together for the benefit of patients, we will have succeeded …
>
> (Bogle 1999)

Is better self-regulation of the profession a crucial part of assuring better quality? If clinical governance is a way of establishing greater accountability of the medical profession (particulary at the local level), then questions arise concerning motives. Some contributors to this book equate greater accountability with an increase in the power of the state at the expense of the medical profession and view this as a political end in itself. Alternatively, accountability may be seen by some as a move to control healthcare professionals and speed up the pace of reform. Or is greater accountability for self-regulated professionals now considered by the public to be a social good in its own right?

Clinical governance and accountability: entwined concepts

The 'official' definition presents clinical governance as a framework for organisational accountability.

> Clinical governance can be defined as a framework through which NHS organisations are accountable for continuously improving the quality of their services and safeguarding high standards of care by creating an environment in which excellence in clinical care will flourish.
>
> (Department of Health 1998)

The tasks of 'continuously improving quality', 'safeguarding standards' and creating the right 'environment for excellence' are wedded to the task of establishing accountability for achieving these goals. Indeed, on this account clinical governance is not so much the process of improving and safeguarding quality but rather the mechanism through which organisations are to be held to account for their efforts.

Policy makers need to ensure that the emphasis on accountability doesn't push out evidence-based approaches to the implementation of systems for quality improvement. If the two concepts have become synonymous then we have to beware muddled thinking. Clinical governance is presented as the local delivery mechanism for changing practice and while accountability for change may be one important component of delivering change, all the evidence shows that accountability alone will not deliver.

Change, particularly clinical and system-wide organisational change, is about hearts and minds, about facilitation, learning and commitment rather than guideline, diktat and accountability. Policy makers and NHS managers will have to trust in local mechanisms for change rather than performance manage every step.

Healthcare accountabilities

At one level, to be accountable means to be responsible for carrying out a particular task and to be able to give an account of one's actions. At another, accountability sets a context that gives work meaning and value. Contained in the concept of assessed accountability are the values against which actions are, either explicitly through systems of appraisal and review or implicitly through an instinctive reference to personal principle and the internalised values of the different healthcare professionals, measured.

The accountabilities of healthcare professionals are complex, potentially contradictory, and unaligned with each other. The way in which each accountability is understood, enacted, and scrutinised is often unclear or fuzzy.

Complexity

Given five minutes, most clinicians in the NHS would identify at least five lines or points of accountability. Accountability to the clinical team, the employing organisation, the profession, the patient and the wider public, and finally the self and often strongly held personal values.

These accountabilities are not presented in any order and indeed one characteristic of this complex web of accountabilities is that different lines of accountability will, for different people, at different times, be more important or relevant than others.

Alignment

In practice, the actual 'account' at the heart of each of these accountabilities to team, organisation, profession, patient, public and self may well be different. Arrangements for monitoring or reviewing the way in which the accountability has been enacted are certainly different depending on which accountability is considered.

For example, the arrangements for local professional self-regulation have, until now, valued individual responsibility, collegial relations and informal controls. Yet the new emphasis within clinical governance is for mechanisms of organisational accountability which emphasise corporate responsibility, managerial relations and formal controls. The challenge for organisations is to mesh these different approaches together (Figure 2.1).

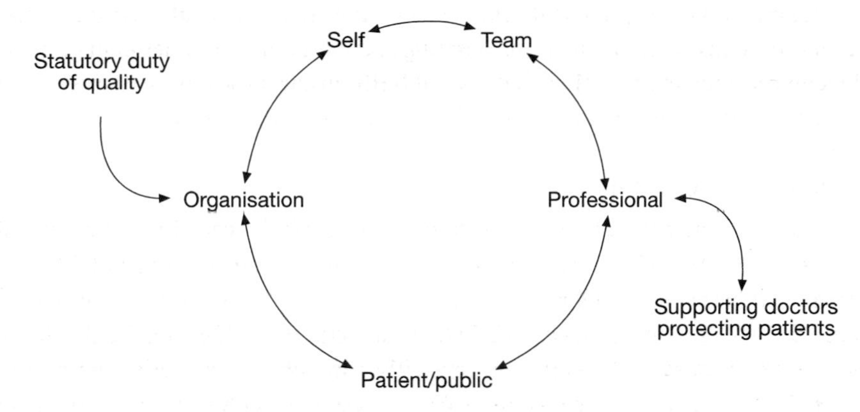

Figure 2.1 Accountabilities and policies working to bring alignment

Fuzziness

Questions are needed to test the strength and clarity of any accountability arrangement. The four questions laid out below look at whether the accountability is clear, managed, fair and authoritative.

1. Is the nature of the accountability clear?
2. Who is responsible for ensuring the accountability is met?
3. What are the criteria for judging if the accountability has been met?
4. What authority is there to deliver or manage the accountability?

When it comes to each of the current five different lines of accountability it would be hard to garner agreement on the answers to each question.

The *Statutory Duty of Quality*

> 'It is the duty of each Health Authority, Primary Care Trust and NHS Trust to put and keep in place arrangements for the purpose of monitoring and improving the quality of healthcare which it provides to individuals.' (Stationary Office 1999)

Answers to the four questions (outlined above) are far from straightforward.

Is the nature of the accountability clear? In essence do trusts, health authorities and primary care trusts (PCTs) know what 'arrangements' to put in place? Would any cursory arrangements suffice in terms of meeting this duty? Or are there specific arrangements that policy makers, government and public should expect to see?

Who is responsible for ensuring the accountability is met? In this case are regional offices, through their performance management functions, the body who should be judging trusts (and chief executives), or will this task effectively rest with CHI? Will PCTs still remain responsible to more strategically orientated health authorities or will this management line disappear?

What are the criteria for judging if the accountability has been met? Making organisations responsible for clinical governance is not necessarily the same as making them responsible for clinical quality. The wording of the duty allows for the possibility that there might be a failure in clinical quality for which the organisation (and presumably the chief executive) might not be held responsible. Would it have been reasonable to expect the organisation to pick up warning signs and act to ensure the failure did not occur? Given that policy on healthcare quality lays out an ambitious ten year plan we have to ask what a *reasonable* state of affairs might look like at this stage.

Looking to the law as it relates to doctors provides two possible interpretations that could well be applied to this new accountability arrangement – the Bolam and the Bolitho test. The Bolam case of 1957 established the principle that a doctor was not guilty of negligence if he (or she) had acted in accordance with a practice accepted by a responsible body of medical men (or women) skilled in that particular art. The Bolitho principle of 1993 modified this position so that the action taken, or not taken, needed also to be supported by rational and cogent reasoning. Which test would best describe the approach that the NHS might take to firing a chief executive for failing to uphold the *Statutory Duty of Quality*?

What authority is there to deliver or manage the accountability? Accountabilities can be categorised into those things that are wholly in the control of the person being made accountable or those goals that are only partially within one's control – objectives that one may play an important part in achieving but cannot deliver on one's own. Is the Statutory Duty of Quality in the former or the latter category, or in both?

Since the duty is for 'arrangements' rather than actual clinical quality it could be argued that the accountability is of the first type and that chief executives already have power to deliver. But, if the nub of the duty is not so much the arrangements but their impact and effectiveness in assuring quality – as it must (from the public's point of view) surely be – then the question remains. Do chief executives have sufficient authority to deliver quality improvement and assurance? And what combination of power and influence over the organisational culture would give them the authority to put effective systems of clinical governance in place?

What impact will this new accountability arrangement have? Will the new power to refer doctors to the National Clinical Assessment Authority when there are concerns over performance effectively give them a new obligation for clinical quality? Up until now Trusts have been performance managed on the basis of financial stability, waiting lists and managing the pressures of emergency admissions. The necessary trade-offs between achieving these potentially conflicting objectives have led to variation in quality, variation in the funding of different services and to explicit or implicit 'rationing'.

One impact of the new statutory duty of quality could be to force out into the open more explicit trade-offs between quality, quantity and cost. These consequences have often been hidden away from public exposure – in a separate world to public expectation and political rhetoric. In theory, this new accountability arrangement could have a significant impact on public expectation and political understanding.

If, for example, organisations have to give an account under the new *Statutory Duty of Quality* then that account will inevitably expose to greater local and public debate key NHS issues of variation, inequity and rationing. Judgements about proper action to monitor and improve quality will – to be fair – need to be informed by this wider context. The duty may potentially blow away the fog that currently hides these crucial decisions away from public gaze.

Supporting Doctors: Protecting Patients

The second set of new accountability arrangements arise from the proposals for modern professional regulation. These pull together plans for revalidation, and the objectives of public accountability, performance assessment and clinical governance. In doing so they attempt to align accountabilities to profession, organisation, and public (three of the five lines of accountability outlined earlier).

The model proposed by *Supporting Doctors: Protecting Patients* and *Assuring the Quality of Medical Practice* the paper starts with the participation of doctors in clinical governance. This participation will, amongst other things, include an annual appraisal. Participation in clinical governance will also provide quantifiable data on performance. This data will form part of the appraisal and any divergence from the results of peers, or an appropriate external standard, might be seen as an indicator of possible problems.

Participation in appraisal and generating the comparative data that will form part of the review process will both be part of a checklist of requirements for the successful five-year revalidation of individual doctors. The appraisal will be a key stage in meeting new organisational requirements for assessing clinical performance and referring any doubts or concerns on to new regional assessment centres.

The comparative data at the heart of this interlinked process will probably be nationally determined in partnership with doctors' relevant colleges. This data may well be made publicly available, thereby introducing an element of public accountability into the new model. It is still unclear what exactly might go into the public domain, and more importantly how the NHS might respond to the understandable wishes of the public to exercise choice on the basis of this information.

Let us test the strength of these new proposed accountabilities by considering four questions outlined earlier.

Is the nature of the accountability clear? The accountability of the doctor to the organisation for the quality of his or her performance is clearly established through the obligation on the clinicians part to take part in clinical governance, audit and appraisal. The accountability of the NHS organisation for reviewing information on performance through these mechanisms is also clear. But the nature of the appraisal and the personal accountability of those undertaking the appraisal of colleagues is still unclear.

Who is responsible for ensuring the accountability is met? At one level the answer is clear – the individual doctor and the trust within which they provide their services. However, there is a lack of clarity about whether health authorities, PCGs or even PCTs will be responsible for implementing appraisal over GPs. It is also unclear who should bear the personal responsibility within the appropriate organisation for enacting this accountability. Nor do we know whether it is clear how those who make others accountable will themselves be made accountable for their role.

What are the criteria for judging if the accountability has been met? It is clear that these accountabilities are two-way, with obligations on the clinician and on the organisation. Criteria for judging if the organisational accountability has been met are not specified. What is to be expected of organisational appraisal systems and how the organisation might fulfil its part of the bargain in addressing the real personal and organisational development issues that are likely to emerge from any sound appraisal mechanism are not spelt out?

What authority is there to deliver or manage the accountability? The system of accountability presented in these proposals makes an important and incorrect presumption that quality can be assured through the assessment of individual performance. But the key to clinical quality often lies in the performance of teams and the way in which whole healthcare systems have a capacity for harm. So if the accountability (on both sides) is really about a new authority to act on any evidence of poor performance, then we have to ask if these accountabilities really take full account of the systemic nature of most avoidable poor outcome?

Conclusion. Clinical governance: enabling excellence or imposing control?

The trouble with 'enabling excellence' is that it sounds like an advertising slogan. It therefore attracts a certain cynical undertow because we know some of the real and very solid barriers to improvement including a lack of money, time and staff.

On the other hand 'imposing control' sounds like a bad thing. At least from the point of view of an independent profession. Unlike the other phrase it is not part of the government lexicon and therefore acts as a subversive alternative – which is always attractive to some.

But do these two options really represent a dichotomy? Are they mutually exclusive? Sending children to school is an act of social control as well as a way of trying to enable a positive outcome which most of the population accepts. Similar arguments could be made in the fields of employment law, the minimum wage, or anti-discrimination legislation – all are controls used as part of the achievement of democratically agreed objectives.

There is a tension between aspects of the clinical governance agenda that stress accountability and those that stress the personal and organisation culture necessary for learning and development. Is clinical governance the means for greater state control over medicine? Or is greater assurance over the performance of medical professionals a pre-requisite to achieving the quality improvement agenda that is at the heart of clinical governance? The implementation of clinical governance may well deliver both in different measures.

Policy initiatives on healthcare quality are re-negotiating the contract between state, medicine and public. And that may well be no bad thing. The trick might be not to leave the politicians or the public out of the equation. Those politicians who lay out grand aspirations for others are also accountable. They have a shared responsibility with healthcare professionals particularly to provide the money, the tools, the trust, the time, and the support that are all necessary for real change.

They also have an accountability to the public. Government confidence about what it is doing on the public's behalf should be based on a sound and active engagement of the public. Government accountability means ensuring that publicly shared values drive such radical change to the NHS and the all-important relationship between patient and healthcare practitioner.

References

Bogle I (1999). So what does clinical governance mean? *Doctor* 64–66

Department of Health (1998). *A First Class Service: Quality in the New NHS.* Leeds: Department of Health

Department of Health (1999). *Supporting Doctors, Protecting Patients: A Consultation Paper on Preventing, Recognising and Dealing with Poor Performance of Doctors in the NHS in England.* Leeds: Department of Health

Department of Health (2000). *Assuring the Quality of Medical Practice.* Leeds: Department of Health

Stationery Office (1999). *Health Act 1999.* London: The Stationery Office Limited

Chapter 3

Clinical governance as a mechanism for implementing national policy: NICE, the National Service Frameworks and CHI

Alison P Hill

Introduction

It has been a concern of successive Health Ministers and Secretaries of State that the NHS is slow or resistant to implement their policies, as Richard Crossman chronicled in his diaries (Crossman 1979). He saw the problem as related to the sheer size of the institution and that its inertia would have been amenable to the influence of his personal power, if only he had been given more time. He and his successors failed to appreciate that the problem lay in the fact that levers capable of exerting power at the level of service provision were largely disconnected from central policymaking. In response to these concerns the NHS Executive was formed, but has itself been found wanting in influencing the widespread and consistent introduction of new ways of working within the service, especially in the realms of clinical care.

The latest attempt to overcome the inertia was the introduction, in 1998, of the policy concept of clinical governance. It is described as a framework for quality management of clinical care and forms part of the modernisation agenda aimed at achieving national consistency in the scope and standards of healthcare provision in the NHS. Clinical governance sits at the heart of the government's blue print for quality assurance and quality improvement in the NHS (Figure 3.1). As a so-called 'local mechanism' for quality assurance and quality improvement it will provide the focus for the centre's inspection into the very heart of clinical practice.

Clinical governance may be a gift for NHS managers, that is, a vehicle or local mechanism to help them do their job. Currently it appears to many to be mystifying and challenging at best, burdensome and worrying at worst.

In order for clinical governance to succeed it must involve an integrated comprehensive and strategic approach to all aspects of local quality management (Figure 3.2). It must be relevant to clinical work. From the government's perspective it must act as a mechanism for implementing national policy and guidance. To penetrate the clinical sphere it must act as a conduit for national level performance management of the service. It must provide the information for performance assessment at national and local levels (Figure 3.1). The National Institute for Clinical Excellence (NICE) and the Commission for Health Improvement (CHI) represent two national devices to support clinical governance. They are typical of the present

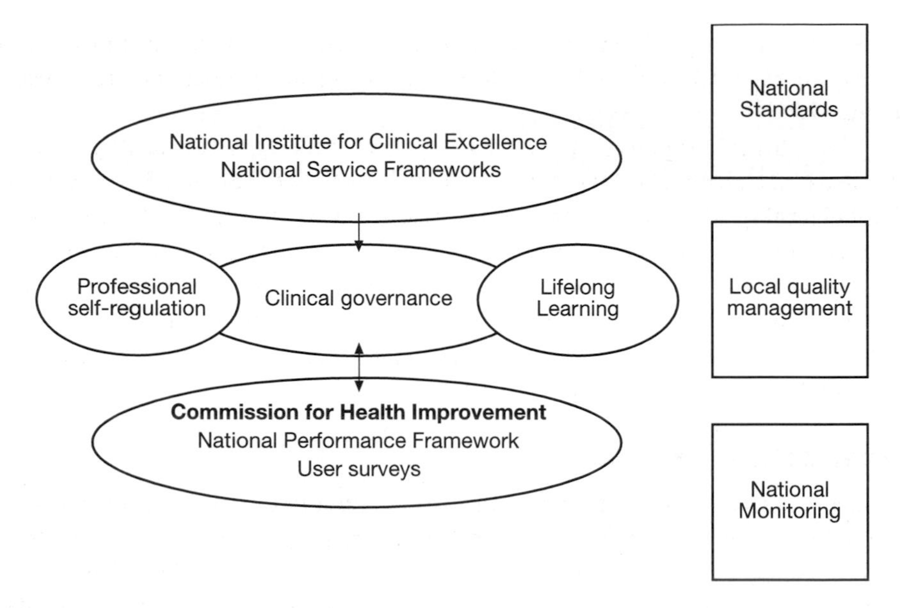

Figure 3.1 The NHS Quality Framework (NHS Executive 1998)

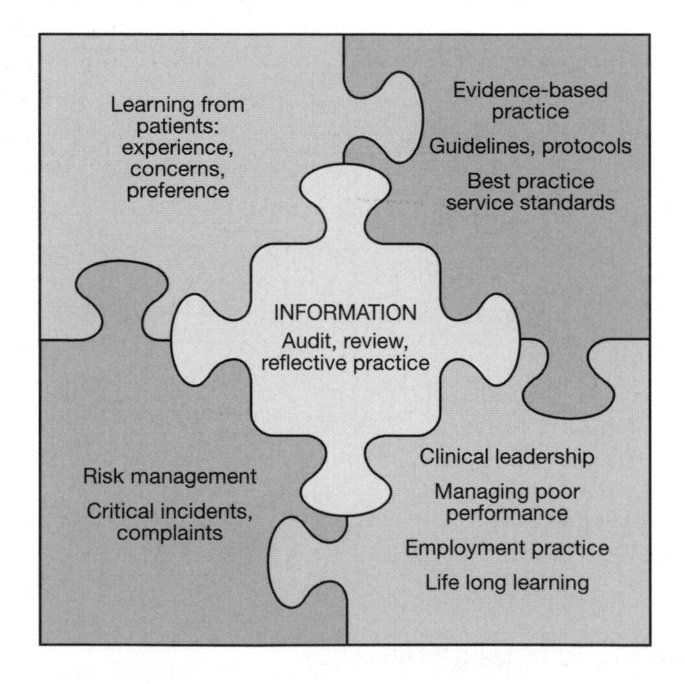

Figure 3.2 The integrated picture of clinical governance

government's policy of central control, which is seen as politicising public sector management. NICE and CHI serve to managerialise the political control process (Power 2000).

This chapter examines the national policy framework for quality and, in particular, the potential roles of NICE, CHI and the National Service Frameworks in local clinical quality management and the tensions likely to emerge between national and local priorities and perspectives. Which will be the strongest driver in changing and improving clinical services: local need, expediency, professional self-interest or the performance management of national priorities? Will clinical governance be a vehicle for the implementation of national guidance, or will national guidance support the development of clinical governance?

Perspectives on quality

Clinical governance is an innocuous term and an aspirational policy that occupies the moral high ground. Clinicians and managers in the NHS are motivated to do their best for patients. But in a complex and bureaucratic health service clinical excellence can be elusive. To what extent can national policy and guidance improve everyday clinical care? Quality assurance involves being able to assess the quality of clinical services and to have systems in place to ensure that the provision of clinical care is as safe and as effective as possible. It involves managing both people and events. It is supported by education and training, clinical audit and good information systems that inform about both process and outcome and that allow the detection and prevention of error. When efficiency is factored into the framework, then systems for assessing and controlling cost are important too. On this perspective, both clinicians and managers would agree.

But quality is in the eye of the beholder. What are the concerns of patients? To get help when they are sick, to be treated by doctors and nurses whom they can trust, to be respected, taken seriously and listened to. Increasingly, they also dislike the patronising behaviour of the traditional professional approach, want to be better informed about their illness and their options and to be seen at a time and place convenient to them. They want treatment that works, the best there is and are increasingly risk averse.

The government wants a service that performs to uniform standards. They want to improve the speed of patients' access to services, to eradicate 'unacceptable' local variation and to have clinical care based more on evidence ('what works').

Implementing clinical governance

If quality assurance is to mean anything, and to allow for improvements in quality, it must somehow incorporate all these perspectives and manage any tensions between them. This is the job of managers in the NHS. The enormity and complexity of this task, the implementation of clinical governance, has led to maxims such as 'starting where you are at', 'go at the pace you can manage' and 'eat the elephant in bite size chunks'. These may have the dubious role of making people feel reassured that the process is feasible and manageable, but the government and the media are baying for demonstrable change. They do not want the service and the people in it to feel comfortable. Local, gentle, piecemeal approaches to improving quality management will not satisfy the government and will not measure up well in the proposed national monitoring exercises. In addition, a piecemeal approach may not take account of the nature of provider organisations and the realities of achieving sustainable change. Increasingly the health system is seen as a living and complex organism, where change in one part can have significant, unforeseen and sometimes negative outcomes. But one thing is certain; the implementation of clinical governance will need to be a developmental process.

Metaphors and similes abound, but they do not really help to conceptualise the process. A model or an exemplar that can be worked through may, however, be helpful. At the end of the summer of 1999, trusts and health authorities had to produce a stocktake of their capacity and capability to implement clinical governance for regional offices of the NHS Executive. Emphasis in national guidance concentrated on structure and processes. In the London region stocktake of NHS trusts, it was clear that different types of organisations were developing systems and processes in a way that was both relevant and easy, based on their culture and their nature. For example, teaching hospitals emphasised hierarchical committee structures, clinical audit and research, community trusts concentrated on empowering and including individuals, emphasising communication, education and training. On the whole, in setting up their governance model they had concentrated on their own, internal mechanisms and perspectives. Very few had thought of ways of involving users or external stakeholders in implementing their quality management, let alone having an input in the design of the systems and processes. Very few had got as far as linking their quality improvement with health authority plans for local health gain (the HImP). Many staff charged with the day-to-day implementation of clinical governance are finding it difficult to know where to focus next. Should they prioritise improving weak components of their systems and processes? Should they work on those services they know are of poorer quality, should they concentrate on those relevant to delivering the HImP? Or how about using the implementation of the latest national service framework?

Evidence-based practice and clinical governance

Evidence

Clinical governance has many components, all of which need to feed into each other (Figure 3.2). The government's ideology admits no uncertainty or variation. Its goal of excellence brooks no debate. Clinical governance is about clinical excellence: 'Doing what works in the right way, at the right time and doing it right every time'.

There is a cherished view that if all clinicians had appropriate skills in critical appraisal and on-line access to scientific journals, they could assess the evidence for themselves in every situation (Sackett *et al.* 1997). There is increasing evidence that, despite their protests, clinicians, particularly GPs, welcome ways of accessing already digested and summarised evidence (McColl *et al.* 1998; Guyatt *et al.* 2000).

Good information about what works underpins the whole notion of clinical governance. The most important processes in clinical governance are the dissemination of this information and review. Information can be spread through education, guidelines and reminders, focused enough to penetrate the frantic world of clinical practice. Individual clinicians and teams need to review what they are doing, and the whole organisation needs to be involved in reflective learning, not only to learn from their mistakes, but to learn how, as a living organisation, they learn and develop their own culture. Governance requires the organisation and its people to have the tools, techniques, discipline and time to become a 'learning organisation' (Davies & Nutley 2000).

The belief that underpins the government's quality policies is that, if only all clinicians would practise according to scientific evidence, then the quality and cost-effectiveness of clinical services would automatically improve, and inequities in access and outcome would disappear. The public is beginning to subscribe to this view. This stance assumes that we have incontrovertible evidence for the detection and treatment of every clinical condition, which of course we do not. The corollary of this belief is that clinicians who do not practise according to evidence are guilty of 'poor practice'.

The problem is that such evidence as there is which might be applicable to a given clinical situation is often inadequate, flawed or equivocal. The randomised controlled trial is thought to provide the most solid evidence on the effectiveness of treatment, but it is drawn from experience under carefully controlled conditions, with highly selected subjects, and gives average or aggregated effects of treatment.

The patient

In addition to the weakness of the centralist, positivist and hyperbolic approach which conflates clinical evidence with 'excellence' is the problem inherent in patients. If patients do not choose to behave according to evidence, to follow the doctor's evidence-based advice, they are deemed to be ill-informed and irrational. There is an increasing view that most patients wish to take an active part in deciding what treatment to employ (shared clinical decision-making), and that given enough information by the health service, they will concur with their doctor's preferred (evidence-based) decision. The problem is that the patient has knowledge and experience gathered and processed in a way that is meaningful to them. The patient has agency and self-determination and priorities which differ from those of the doctor or of the state. Patients, and those around them have to want the treatment in the first place, remember to take it, take it in the right way and at the right time, fit it in with their lives and put up with the side-effects.

We still do not know how to arrive at clinical decisions by involving patients in the process (Protheroe *et al.* 2000) and this presents a problem for those who hold such a positivist view of quality in clinical practice. But government policy exhorts the service to become more responsive to the needs and concerns of patients. Is this hypocrisy, or merely a misunderstanding?

Experience

The third problem is the power of experience and expertise in the clinician. The essence of professional practice is the ability and preparedness to apply an increasing set of skills to differing and complex situations, to integrate knowledge and technical skill with understanding. At worst, emphasising the importance of experience can be used to justify adherence to subjective preference, prejudice and ignorance. At best, it involves understanding the unique clinical, social and psychological circumstances of the individual patient, and combining that with an understanding of how an intervention works in real life, its advantages and its drawbacks.

Really effective practice brings together and resolves the tensions between research-based evidence, clinical 'real' world experience (expertise) and the preferences of patients and their carers. Increasingly, the clinician's powers of persuasion are becoming an important factor, hiding under the term 'good communication skills'. If a patient chooses not to take the course of action suggested by the best available scientific evidence, will the doctor be guilty of 'poor practice'?

The trouble with guidelines

For many years now, attempts to inform clinical practice about the latest 'best evidence' have been in the form of clinical guidelines (Table 3.1). There is now a whole discipline of medical science aimed at the proper processes by which guidelines should be drawn up (Cluzeau *et al.* 1999), and further research and development effort aimed at the tricky business of implementing them (Dowie *et al.* 1998). It seems very difficult to persuade clinicians to change their practice. This is more marked with older clinicians and with those who attend fewer formal continuing education sessions. Even if guidelines are used that are drawn up according to best practice, they often fail to have impact. There may be many reasons for this. It may be that despite the guideline being available, the practitioner lacks basic knowledge of the evidence on which the guideline is based. It may be that practitioners know the evidence but do not believe it. It may be that they know of and believe the evidence but do not see it as relevant to their practice, or to the individual sitting in front of them. And it may well be that doctors, in their desire to please their patients (in order to encourage their return) assume that the patient wants a course of action other than that suggested by guidelines. The doctor does what he believes

Table 3.1 Clinical guidance documents defined

Guidelines: systematically developed statements that assist decision-making about appropriate care for a specific clinical condition
Protocols: More detailed development of these statements for local application
Standards of care: Authoritative statements about minimum, or excellent, levels of performance required.

the patient most desires. This is difficult to measure experimentally, but is an explanation increasingly appearing in qualitative research on treatment decisions.

In devising guidelines it is clearly important that their content is meaningful, credible and recognisable to clinicians, to patients and to managers.

It is generally recommended that a variety of different techniques are used to disseminate and support the implementation of guidelines, no one current method being more effective in general terms than any other. It is likely that there is a cultural aspect to the extent to which guidelines are accepted, and strong contextual influences on the likelihood of their being adhered to and the consistency and sustainability of any change they may initiate (Freemantle 2000). Observational studies of the evidence-based medicine field suggest that the implementation of guidelines needs strong local leadership, a sense of direction, tolerance of uncertainty and a flexible, multi-faceted approach. It is messy, non-linear, full of frustration and may have unintended consequences.

National mechanisms for local control

One of the problems with the clinical guidelines industry and the contestabilility of evidence is that there is confusion in the field. There is too much local variation in the content of guidelines, delay and lack of co-ordination over prioritising the evidence that is robust enough to be implemented throughout the NHS, and lack of consistency on the priorities chosen by health authorities when deciding to fund innovations. The Government's solution was to invent the National Institute for Clinical Excellence. Quickly dubbed the National Institute for Cost-Effectiveness, its prime role was seen by the service to be rationing new treatments rather than rationalising the use of better established ones. NICE is aimed at producing national consistency in devising guidelines, and co-ordinating national audits of clinical outcomes (Table 3.2).

Will the fact that there is a national programme for the development and implementation of evidence-based guidelines mean that practice becomes more evidence-based? On the evidence presented both by research evidence and observation in daily practice, the answer is that it is not that simple.

Table 3.2 Functions of NICE and CHI

NICE functions
- Evaluate new technologies
- Clinical guidelines: assess existing ones, commission new ones
- Create referral protocols
- Devise and co-ordinate audit programmes

CHI functions
- Lead clinical governance
- Review local implementation of NSF and NICE guidelines
- Undertake systematic reviews of clinical governance
- Investigate problems
- Undertake special enquiries in the NHS

In recognition of this the government has also set up the Commission for Health improvement. CHI is an arm's length body set up to support and monitor the introduction of clinical governance (Table 3.2). According to the Health Act 1999, the functions of the Commission are to provide advice and information by which NHS provider trusts can monitor and improve the quality of healthcare they provide. It would do this through undertaking regular reviews and reporting on the systems and procedures for clinical governance arrangements in trusts. On the other hand, when CHI was launched in October 1999, the Prime Minister's press statement suggested a more draconian approach. He seemed to be suggesting an Ofsted type of inspectorate:

> The Commission will monitor directly the quality of care provided by trusts, listen to patient's complaints and make sure they are dealt with properly, make sure all areas of the NHS are using drugs and technologies recommended in national guidelines, spread good practice and help to weed out bad practice.

Already there is a tension between its preferred approach to take a developmental and supportive role, and the expectations of ministers. Their exhortations that it should 'root out' bad practice, 'name and shame' those that fall short of national standards or who fail to implement national guidance appear almost daily in the press.

One thing is certain: trends for implementing national guidance, developing local quality standards and audit will be set through CHI's routine inspections. Trusts will concentrate on what CHI inspectors want to see. Early indications are that they are less worried about the slavish adherence to guidelines and more concerned about what actually happens to patients (Morant 2000). CHI intends to collect data and reports from the trusts, and draw up a picture of what is going on. But will inspection focus on potentially troublesome areas appearing in the self-assessments sent in by trusts, or will CHI employ a systematic framework for each review visit? This, for example, could be the National Service Frameworks and an established set of NICE guidelines once they become available.

The problem is that these do not necessarily lend themselves to providing either a framework for inspection or evidence of progress and achievement, nor of the extent to which patient experience has improved. The indicators CHI develops to assess progress in clinical governance will be crucial in the development of clinical governance on the ground. What is examined will determine where Trusts work hardest and provide best evidence of their activity and achievement. Will this be the best approach to improving the experiences of patients? Unless these national policy planks are strategically planned and co-ordinated, designed to be compatible and cover a broad range of issues, the service will be confused. Attention will be focused on spurious priorities and evidence confined to the easily observed and measurable.

National Service Frameworks

The first National Service Framework (NSF) was the Calman-Hine model for cancer services, published in 1995 (Department of Health 1995). It was concerned with improving the access of patients to the best possible care. This framework was drawn up after a lengthy consultation process within the service and with patients' groups. It proposed that common cancers should be treated at district general hospitals but complicated or rare cases should be treated in specialised cancer centres. A multidisciplinary approach to the diagnosis and management of cancer was recommended. The model was sketchy in outline, dealt in some detail with the more common cancers, and has developed in concept and specificity over the succeeding years. It concentrated on the active treatment of cancers, and did not really detail an integrated model that would include prevention, rehabilitation and palliative care. Its implementation was impeded by the arguments of vested interests aimed at preserving the status quo of services configuration. The disaggregation of local cancer services, particularly in radiology and surgery, has proved difficult. It has been hard to develop communication and exchange between the cancer centres and peripheral units. Service reconfiguration and cross-boundary, patient centred models of care are now developing more as the result of 'bottom-up' engagement of clinicians than was possible by decommissioning local services during the days of the internal market.

The NSF for mental health appeared next, in 1999. This was met with cries of dismay from the service. Far from being seen as helpful, it was seen as an aspirational document that was impossible to achieve within current resource constraints and in the context of so many trust reconfigurations in mental health.

The third, for coronary heart disease, was produced after a lengthy consultation and development process involving many stakeholders. In contrast to the other frameworks, it has incorporated more of the current evidence on effective treatment as well as best practice in service configuration and delivery. It approaches the vast area of cardiac disease prevention and management using a framework based on a cardiac patient's life journey, and breaks the advice on implementation up into recognisably discrete sections and practical steps. It gives a (possibly unrealistic but definite) timetable for implementation. Most importantly from the point of view of the arguments of this paper, it does not rely on any current internal quality assurance mechanisms for its implementation. It is particular and specific and it gives a clear indication of where professional consensus sees the balance of evidence on cost-effectiveness to lie.

Clinical governance in most trusts and PCGs is not sufficiently far advanced as a comprehensive and integrated system to deliver such a massive hike in the quality (in all its aspects) and comprehensiveness of services to patients with cardiac disease. But the framework's detailed and integrated description of service configuration, and its targets for delivering effective care may form the basis of an implementation strategy for clinical governance locally. This is because the framework requires not only the widespread and consistent use of effective treatment, monitored through regular clinical audit, but also the joint working of stakeholders and agencies across organisational boundaries, and incorporates the patient's perspective. So is this what clinical governance has been waiting for?

A slippery path to quality improvement

The coronary heart disease framework provides 12 standards covering the prevention, detection, treatment and rehabilitation of ischaemic heart disease (angina, myocardial infarct and related heart failure). It provides a number of goals aimed at saving lives through faster more comprehensive treatment. Its targets are reductions in mortality rates. It involves some quick wins, which involve the processes rather than the outcome of service, for example: the setting up of smoking cessation clinics, rapid access chest pain assessment clinics, and reducing 'call to needle time'(the delay in getting thrombolytic treatment after a myocardial infarction). The problem with this confident set of documents is that it implies that making the described service changes, and meeting the goals will reduce cardiac mortality. Unfortunately life is not that simple. The framework depends for its delivery on complex changes in already complex systems, and, above all, it will depend on the action of real people. Much of the recommended change is based on evidence from clinical trials. We know the treatment can work, but will it work in real life? If call to needle time is reduced, will the attention to this particular chain of events result in inattention and a reduction in quality somewhere else in the system? If it does, will it be possible to spot this and to find out why?

Implementation may be slow and problematic. Take for example the standards aimed mainly at primary care (Standards 3 and 4). These involve the measures to be taken to prevent myocardial infarct in high-risk groups. Ten per cent of the British population fall into these categories. In some areas where deprivation is high and lower social classes form a large proportion of the population, it will be much higher than this. At present those most at risk are under-treated whilst treatment is often given to those whose risk for suffering a myocardial infarct is relatively low. Some of this is due to the fact that many GPs and most members of the public do not appreciate how the various predictors of the disease interact in a complex way to determine an individual's risk. These include raised age, gender, blood pressure, smoking, abnormal blood lipid ratios, diabetes, and the presence of symptomatic ischaemic heart disease. Preventative measures, including the prescription of relatively new and expensive medicines, should be targeted at those with a high individual (combined) risk (the absolute risk). The aim of treatment is to reduce that absolute risk.

To help doctors identify those at the greatest risk, tools are being developed. These involve charts. There are three main ones in existence (Jackson 2000a). The Sheffield Table, the New Zealand (Jackson 2000b) and the Joint British Chart (British Cardiac Society *et al.* 2000) assess risk based on combined risk factors, but present the information in different ways. They are all derived from the Framingham Heart Study, a large scale, longitudinal study in Framingham USA, which followed a largely white population over many years. They are designed to be put on the surgery wall so that a doctor can refer to them during a consultation in which risk is assessed and decisions about treatment are made. But they are hedged about with many caveats. They are inaccurate at the edges of the risk bands and in low risk. They underestimate the risk in people who have left ventricular hypertrophy (damage to the heart muscle caused by high blood pressure), Asians who come from the Indian subcontinent and patients who have inherited conditions which cause some patterns of raised blood lipids. The NSF recommends using risk assessment tables and decision support. But it is not easy. The same week that the NSF was published, the *British Medical Journal* devoted a whole issue to cardiovascular disease. In one study all three of the charts mentioned above were sent to samples of GPs and practice nurses in different sequence (Isles *et al.* 2000). They were asked to apply them to 12 standardised case histories. This was therefore a paper exercise, so it did not include the distractions, contradictions and complexity of a live consultation with a real patient. In this study the Sheffield Table proved to be the most difficult to use. Another study dealing with the management of hypertension (a risk factor for cardiac disease) compared the use of a risk table combined with a computer-based decision support system, the table alone or neither ('usual care') (Montgomery *et al.* 2000). In this study the cardiovascular risk and the blood pressure in these hypertensive patients were not reduced any more successfully in the group using computer-based decision support. These papers tell us that it is as important to have evidence on the effectiveness of implementation strategies as it is to have evidence on new treatments. In finding ways to support the implementation of the Framework it is vital to ask: can it work? does it work? is it worth it?

Another example of the large hurdles to be overcome in implementation is the Standard dealing with reducing 'call to needle time'. If thrombolytic drugs are given after a myocardial infarct to dissolve the blood clot causing obstruction in the coronary arteries, lives can be saved. The earlier these drugs can be given, the greater the reduction in mortality (Fibrinolytic Therapy Trialists Collaborative Group 1994). Leaving out the time taken for the patient or bystander to realise there is something amiss and to summon help there are many stages at which delay can occur.

First, should the GP be called? Some GPs can assess the situation and give first aid. In some rural areas the doctor may arrive faster than an ambulance. But for most people, calling a GP adds to the delay. The ambulance needs to be properly equipped with highly trained paramedics, and carry life-supporting equipment. Getting to hospital fast is not the only consideration. Defibrillation, morphine to relieve pain and to control shock, oxygen and aspirin may be life saving in those first few minutes. In order to meet the response time, targets in the NSF show how many more ambulances in any service will have to be suitably staffed and equipped. What will prioritising this part of the service mean for other patients in urgent need of ambulance transport? Only one third of accident and emergency departments currently provide thrombolysis. Most do not have the required skill mix, the training, the ability to make an accurate diagnosis of myocardial infarction and to assess the safety of giving the drug in any individual care. They need the capacity and equipment to maintain supplies of the drug. Cutting down delay is not simple or cheap. Feasibility, logistics and opportunity cost are all-important considerations.

Managing change and conflicting priorities

It is now a statutory duty for senior managers in NHS providers to assure the quality of clinical services. Although clinical governance may eventually provide the mechanism by which they implement national policy and co-ordinate it with local policy, it is not yet sufficiently sophisticated. It cannot deliver the requirements and changes in service provision described in the cardiac NSF without increased resources, substantial changes in workforce numbers, deployment and skill mix. Better routine data related to the activities and outcomes specified within the NSF are vital, as are new research evidence on effectiveness and on robust, relevant outcome measures.

On the contrary, the NSF for coronary heart disease offers trusts a focus for trying out the structures and functions of clinical governance. Overwhelmed by the volume of guidance and by conflicting priorities the latest NSF provides an attractive place to begin. But as we have seen this approach has inherent problems.

People may respond to clear guidance if those actions recommended seem plausible and possible. But over-reliance on set guidelines has several problems. First, process is easier to effect and to measure than outcomes. Secondly, provider organisations are living systems. Change in one may have unforeseen and adverse effects in another. Guidelines, and to a greater degree NSFs are complex interventions. We simply do not know if implementing them will have the desired effects of reducing mortality. Thirdly, over-reliance on guidelines may lead to the suspension of critical thought, so crucial to good professional practice. It could lead to the fossilisation of medical scientific knowledge and to the undervaluing and eventual attrition of professional expertise. There is a danger that, under the watchful eye of CHI, the clinician asks 'Did I follow the guideline right' rather than 'Is the treatment working?' or 'Is this the best we can do?' Lastly the sheer weight of NICE guidelines may overwhelm the service before it knows how to implement them.

It is difficult to defend the rhetoric of clinical freedom against increasing public lack of tolerance towards 'indifferent', 'scientised' 'ignorant', 'incompetent' and above all 'arrogant' doctors. Loss of respect on both sides has resulted in the production of guidelines and inspection as remedies. Yet patients' expectations and preferences are missing from the centralist model.

Part of CHI's task is to identify and target deliverables that are achievable and this will satisfy ministers while the real work of effecting change goes on. It is too soon to hold chief executives to account if the NSFs fail to deliver their goals. The centre must recognise the complexity and difficulty of managing clinical quality. If clinical governance is to be a locally owned, integrated, strategically planned and comprehensive approach to clinical quality assurance and improvement, it must be supported by a strategically planned and integrated national programme of guidance and support.

References

British Cardiac Society *et al.* (2000). Joint British recommendations on prevention of coronary heart disease in clinical practice: summary. *British Medical Journal* **320**, 705–708

Cluzeau F, Littlejohns J, Grimshaw JM, Feder G. Moran S (1999). Development of a generic methodology to assess the quality of clinical guidelines. *International Journal of Quality in Healthcare* **1**, 21–28

Crossman RHS (1979). In Howard A (ed.) *The Crossman Diaries*

Davies H & Nutley SM (2000.) Developing learning organisations in the new NHS. *British Medical Journal* **320**, 998–1001

Dowie R (1998). A review of research in the United Kingdom to evaluate the implementation of clinical guidelines in general practice. *Family Practice* **15**, 462–470

Dowie R, Jones R, Robinson M (1998). Research on guideline implementation in primary care. *Family Practice* **17**, s5

Expert Advisory Group (1995). *A Framework for Commissioning Cancer Services* London: Department of Health

Fibrinolytic Therapy Trialists Collaborative Group (1994). Indications for fibrinolytic therapy in suspected myocardial infarction: collaborative overview of early mortality and major morbidity results from randomised controlled trials of more than 1000 patients. *Lancet* **343**, 311–322

Freemantle N (2000). Implementation strategies. *Family Practice* **17**, s7–s10

Guyatt GH, Meade MO, Jaeschke RZ, Cooke DJ, Haynes RB (2000). Practitioners of evidence based care. *British Medical Journal* **320**, 945

Isles CG, Ritchie LD, Murchie P, Norrie J (2000). Risk assessment in primary prevention of coronary heart disease: randomised comparison of three scoring methods. *British Medical Journal* **320**, 690–691

Jackson R (2000a). Guidelines in preventing cardiovascular disease in clinical practice. *British Medical Journal* **320**, 659–660

Jackson R (2000b). Updated New Zealand cardiovascular risk-benefit prediction guide. *British Medical Journal* **320**, 709–710

McColl A, Smith H, White P, Field J (1998). General Practitioners perceptions of the route to evidence based medicine: a questionnaire survey. *British Medical Journal* **316**, 361–5

Montgomery AA, Fahey T, Peters TJ, MacIntosh C, Sharp DJ (2000). Evaluation of computer based clinical decision support system and risk chart for management of hypertension in primary care: randomised controlled trial. *British Medical Journal* **320**, 686–689

Morant H (2000). Patients will be paramount in assessments says CHI. *British Medical Journal* **320**, 1294

NHS Executive (1998). *A First Class Service.* London: HMSO

Power M (2000). The evolution of the audit society, its politics of control and the advent of CHI. In Miles A, Hampton JR & Hurwitz B (eds) *NICE, CHI and the NHS Reforms: Enabling Excellence or Imposing Control.* London: Aesculapius Medical Press, pp127–137

Protheroe J, Fahey T, Montgomery M, Peters TJ (2000). The impact of patient preferences on the treatment of atrial fibrillation: observational study of patient based decision analysis. *British Medical Journal* **320**, 1380–1384

Sackett DI, Richardson SR, Rosenberg W, Haynes RB (1997). *Evidence-based Medicine: How to Practice and Teach EBM.* London: Churchill Livingstone

Chapter 4

Governance as a local mechanism for the early detection and minimisation of medical error: defining the role and methods of critical incident reporting, risk management and whistle blowing

Maureen Dalziel

Introduction

Questions about quality are neither new nor limited to healthcare. By virtue of the communications revolution, education and consumer organisations, people have become better informed and more interested in issues of quality, and individual and collective expectations have risen dramatically. Traditionally neither national experts nor local managers regularly assessed and controlled the quality of local clinical practice. But improvements to the quality of care are one of the underlying principles of *The New NHS – Modern and Dependable* (Department of Health 1997), the thrust of *A First Class Service* (Department of Health 1998) and *The NHS Plan* (Department of Health 2000).

The government's proposed partnerships with clinicians, which will involve setting national standards and introducing a system of clinical governance to ensure that they are delivered locally is aimed at achieving greater consistency in clinical care. It builds on over a decade's pursuit of initiatives that have targeted clinical care improvement. These initiatives include clinical audit, changes to the curricula for the undergraduate training of health professionals, the ethos of continuing professional development and, more recently, the emphasis on clinical effectiveness and an evidence-based approach to care.

Many different processes were adapted and used to deliver these initiatives, so it is not surprising that the results to date have been mixed and leave commentators critical and many with perceptions of inconsistent progress.

The modernising agenda of this government believes that clinical governance is the framework for clinical quality improvement through which it can safeguard high standards of care and encourage an enthusiasm for improvement. It is the means by which NHS organisations ensure the provision of quality clinical care by making individuals accountable for setting, maintaining and monitoring performance standards. To be successful it needs to build upon present systems and processes and to make use of previous knowledge. Furthermore it needs to be part of the corporate governance agenda if it is truly to impact on performance.

Healthcare risk

In the 21st century, more individuals are aware of the fallibility of the healthcare intervention: it is not risk free. Increasingly there is greater awareness and demands for better management of clinical risk, but only those who are naive believe that risk management mechanisms and methods will eliminate error. In truth, only a proportion of adverse incidents can be avoided even in those industries or organisations that systematically assess, review and seek ways to prevent their occurrence. At present, any assessment in healthcare is based on subjective judgements and unbiased pictures cannot be obtained, as not all events are recorded. However, despite these limitations, lessons can and should be learnt from mistakes.

Clinical risk management

Clinical risk management is a means of reducing risks from adverse events by systematic examination and seeking ways to prevent occurrences in the future (Vincent 2001). It is at an early stage of development, although it is seen as part of a process that could reduce clinical litigation bills within the NHS which, through the litigation authority's risk pooling schemes, monitor trusts' performance against agreed clinical risk standards.

At present, some 40 per cent of NHS trusts are unable to meet the risk management standards expected by the Clinical Negligence Scheme for trusts which has been in existence for five years. This shortfall continues even as these standards are incorporated into the NHSE Controls Assurance initiative, which is the NHS's overall response to risk for Corporate Governance requirements. Among the reasons for this are that these standards have not been seen as an NHS priority and have not had sufficient financial incentives or sanctions for them to be taken up by more NHS trusts. Furthermore, as organisations merge, the capability of one another can dilute. In some cases this means that those who have been able to meet the standards may fall down during the merger process.

Getting clinical risk management to work well needs more than just standard setting, standard forms and small financial penalties. It requires local expertise to undertake risk management assessments and develop monitoring processes. It needs to be linked to patients' complaints and other risk management systems such as health and safety. If local organisations are to meet the needs of governance through the management of medical errors they will need to ensure that their clinicians are persuaded to accept the importance of standard setting and monitoring. They need to have medical staff who establish clinical standards informed, of course, by national requirements and research evidence but also by patients and those that commission their services and by their own experience. But organisations need more than just enthusiastic and willing staff: they need to demonstrate explicit accountability mechanisms and operational processes that show a trail from the individual to the board.

Clinical risk management should be comprehensive, not confined to one department, and it needs to show that it can have an impact on the quality of care. Furthermore, it requires an open environment so that staff can be encouraged to report critical events, learn from their experience and be open rather than defensive in dealing with patients. It needs to be led by senior clinicians with the backing of the trust board in a spirit of 'so what needs to be different as a result' and for the recommendations to be considered and implemented quickly. For risk management to become more commonplace it will need to be embraced by primary care as well as hospital and community trusts.

For risk management to function realistically, critical incident analysis also needs to be set in a context of what is unexpected or exceptional. In other words, how frequent or how rare is the critical incident, not only within the unit, but also across the NHS. Otherwise, there is a danger that analysis of clinical error becomes dominated by populist or legal opinions of perfection, or public expectations about acceptability. Few individuals welcome being held to account through a process of public shaming and blaming rather than through processes that support an ethos of constructive learning and risk management (Dalziel 1999).

At the moment it is not possible to take on board comparisons except though the use of the results of confidential enquiries and audits. In the UK, these processes are confined to certain areas such as peri-operative care, (Buck *et al.* 1987), still births and intensive care and not all parts of healthcare. Future potential sources of this sort of information could be the National Institute for Clinical Excellence (NICE), Commission for Health Improvement, the Audit Commission, the National Care Standards Commission and the NHS Litigation Authority.

Learning from errors

Organisations can identify clinical risk factors from incidents that have been the subject of complaints, litigation, to inform clinical risk management, training, and staffing strategies at a local level and across the NHS (IMLAB 1999).

In every clinical speciality there are examples of failings that, if targeted, may help to develop ways to reduce risks to patients and staff. The following examples illustrate the potential that systematic analysis of cases has for learning and reducing risk.

Mental health

Over the past few years a number of mental health services have been subjected to public scrutiny and debate as a result of adverse incident investigations. The themes that emerge from these exhaustive investigations are common. Failings include whole health system failures that have arisen from poor communication, lack of leadership and absence of written and practical protocols. The delivery of care in mental health illness is complex, it requires good working relations at many different levels of the health and social care system from national to community level. Delivering care systems in mental health needs processes and systems that can monitor performance effectively.

Joint agency working will assist inter-agency communication and encourage co-operation between health and social care services. Joint professional development, education and training programmes can support local staff within health, social and voluntary care sectors, understand their responsibilities and handle the different expectations within a hospital, mental health unit, community or primary care setting. The local authority, health authority, trust boards and primary care groups should address communication and training during the local implementation of the National Service Framework for mental health. However, even with solid operational policies and processes and good leadership, patients and staff will continue to operate within an environment of risk, even if it is less risky than before. Apart from ensuring operational policies and procedures are in place and are updated to reflect lessons learnt from enquiries, extra vigilance will always be needed in those areas where the systems have failed in the past.

Obstetrics

In any one year, actuarial predictions show that up to 60 per cent of clinical litigation expenditure within the NHS arises from brain damage at birth (NHSLA 1999). The scale of awards will continue to rise substantially if the courts consider that investing in the stock market is subject to too many risks and make awards using assumptions about less risky investments. At today's settlement level a 1 per cent fall in brain injury cases would lead to five less brain damaged babies through negligence, a saving of over £7.5 million per annum for the NHS. This means that any action to reduce risk is worthwhile, not only for the sake of these children and their parents, but also for the NHS.

Birth brain injury claims (Ennis & Vincent 1990) show the following common findings:

1. The absence of adequate supervision of the delivery process: this may mean no access to a consultant obstetrician or it may mean the absence of a senior consultant or midwife in the delivery process when complications are known to be present.
2. Inadequate or inappropriate action taken as a result of a cartographic (CTG) trace: the time taken to deliver baby was prolonged or the mode of delivery itself using interventions and instruments such as forceps, ventouse or caesarean section was inappropriately carried out leading to damage.
3. Errors in the administration of drugs such as Syntometrine.

If there is inadequate recording of the process of care and clinical decision making within the medical records or if the records are missing or not complete, this means that actions will not be able to be defended.

Reducing the risk of brain injury to babies and achieving change in obstetric processes are major challenges for NHS trusts and obstetric units. Leadership and the monitoring and management of operational processes and procedures that have closer supervision of junior obstetricians and midwives and better communication will be essential. Training of trust obstetric and midwifery staff is needed on CTG trace interpretation, team building and case note recording.

Anaesthetics

A five-country European study that analysed over 300 closed medical negligence claims identified common factors which should inform future strategies to inform risk, increase patient safety and decrease claims frequency. To reduce risk further, improvements were needed to pre- and post-operative assessment processes, routine checking and monitoring of equipment, blood transfusion and medication. Other improvements were needed to the supervision of staff and documentation of records (Goodwin & Green 1997).

Patient concerns

Case studies from the medical protection organisations identify that doctors and health professionals should pay special attention to communication, particularly if the results are less than perfect or if there are unexpected complications. If a patient reports a lesion in cases such as suspected breast cancer, clinicians should consider routine follow-up even if the diagnostic tests are negative, as reliance on these sorts of tests is not foolproof.

Anger from patients is a common indicator that the patient will seek retribution in the courts. Informed consent is part of the communication process and physicians personally should discuss any proposed treatment with patients and their families. This discussion should include the reasons for treatment, expected and potential unexpected outcomes, the risks of treatment, the treatment alternatives and the risks and description of one or more possible outcomes.

Common problems in defending claims include inadequate documentation of patients' medical records: records must be legible, typed or transcribed where possible and generated contemporaneously and free of offensive comments. Altering records often means the discrediting of the evidence in the case notes. If an alteration is required it is important that it is in the form of an addendum that is dated and signed.

The development of staff and the organisation

An essential part of the success of governance at the local level will depend on the staff and organisations that deliver care. Few mechanisms work without motivated staff with high morale. Investment will be required to develop the local organisations' capacity and capability. In each organisation there is a need for general awareness.

It needs more than just reliance on the individual responsibilities of clinicians. Staff have a personal responsibility to ensure their own high standards but organisations have a responsibility for generating a culture which promotes and rewards learning rather than apportioning blame and punishment. This organisational environment will be necessary if clinicians are to be encouraged to overcome their reluctance in this matter. Matters of error management need clinical leadership, board championship and technical competence by individuals. Formal levers such as a whistle blowing policy and explicit responsibility within job descriptions to report on poor performance will also be required. Organisations will need to have humane exit strategies and the necessary expertise to handle those who have not responded to training. In other words, organisational processes and accountability for these initiatives will need to be in place. Apart from forms, rules and technical experts at the local level, the processes of investigating and managing medical errors must be seen as an integral part of the process of delivering healthcare in the organisation and not as an end in itself.

The management of clinical error is much more than a collection of processes and systems. As illustrated by the case studies, the necessary organisation culture to reduce clinical error has to be founded on team work, principles of collaboration and the sharing of information and expertise, not only within clinical networks but with health managers and other professionals. Leadership is essential. In more and more professionals this essential skill needs to be nurtured. Most organisations will, from time to time, need to draw on expert advice from outside until sufficient competence is developed in these areas.

Executive boards will be the guardian of the organisation's culture and will need to understand how to negotiate and trade off clinical, financial and corporate governance. It is a big challenge to get the balance right between individual clinical freedom and judgement, public expectations and the demands of corporate accountability. Each health and social care organisation will have to consider how to address this. Organisations have their own context and many will have shared governance and accountability arrangements with others.

Conclusions

1. It is unrealistic to expect an error free health system and the detection of medical error and public investigation is insufficient on its own to effect change and raise healthcare standards.
2. As part of governance at a local level, organisations need systems and processes that can identify errors and boards that are accountable.
3. To take on board the risks identified and lessons learnt and to implement the change required needs organisations with leaders, processes and procedures and staff training that is targeted to reduce risk.

4. Continual monitoring of the uptake and compliance of any changes that are introduced should be incorporated into any subsequent change programme.
5. Clinical staff need to keep up-to-date in their clinical practice and apply this knowledge in the interests of their patients. Effective communication and information flow between all those involved in a patient's case and good administrative processes and comprehensive contemporaneous medical records are important facets of reducing risk to patients.

Recommendations

1. All local organisations should have a process for learning from medical errors and managing clinical risk.
2. Structurally, each organisation needs an executive director who reports directly to the board for governance and chairs a sub committee that is responsible for investigating critical incidents and managing risk. This should include agreed written procedures into the investigation of complaints, adverse events and incidents.
3. Each organisation should have a separate confidential process to safeguard and promote whistle blowing. This is traditionally within the remit of appointing a non-executive director who would be the guardian of the whistle blowing process and policy.
4. Each organisation should use the lessons learnt from risk management and adverse events to update local operational policies, fashion local training and monitor that the new processes and policies are implemented.

References

Buck N, Devlin HB, Lunn JN (1987). *The Report of a Confidential Enquiry into Perioperative Deaths.* London: The Nuffield Provincial Hospitals Trust, the King's Fund

Dalziel M (1999). 'Testing testing'. How one region is getting to grips with clinical governance. *Health Management*

Department of Health (1998). *A First Class Service.* London: The Stationery Office

Department of Health (2000). *The NHS Plan. A Plan for Investment. A Plan for Reform.* London: The Stationery Office

Department of Health (1997). *The New NHS – Modern and Dependable.* London: The Stationery Office

Ennis M & Vincent CA (1990). Obstetric accidents: a review of 64 cases. *British Medical Journal* **300**, 1365–1367

Goodwin H & Green S (1997). *Anaesthetic Study.* London: Europa Medica Risk Management Services

Institute of Medicine, Law and Bioethics (IMLAB) (1999). *The Impact of Consultants Medico-legal and Complaints Work on the NHS. Report of a Steering Group.* Liverpool and Manchester: IMLAB

NHSLA (1999). *Annual Report.* London: NHS Litigation Authority

Vincent C (2001). *Clinical Risk Management,* 2nd edn. London: BMJ Books

Chapter 5

Governance as a local mechanism for ensuring continuing professional education and development

Shelley Heard and Elisabeth Paice

Introduction

Professional education and development are key strategies in the delivery of the clinical governance agenda. It is unlikely that governance will be the mechanism that ensures that professionals continue to develop to the benefit of patient care; far more likely is that continuing professional development (CPD) will ensure the delivery of high standards of healthcare through accountable professionals. *A First Class Service – Quality in the New NHS* (Department of Health 1998) established the importance of lifelong learning and its association with clinical governance. This document set professional development within the context of clinical governance and by so doing gave it a political credibility that acknowledges its importance and its potential call upon resources. For doctors, continuing professional development is more than keeping up-to-date on medical issues (CME) (Table 5.1).

Lifelong learning must also be an organisational concept. It requires that individuals who are committed to lifelong learning and ongoing professional development are recruited into the NHS and then, are enabled by organisations to achieve it. The NHS and its constituent organisations need therefore to value professional development sufficiently to resource it with respect to both time and funding.

Within this context, serious concerns have been raised about professional education within today's healthcare systems. Increasing specialisation and service demands on both senior and junior doctors have fragmented and eroded the education community, impairing the transfer of professional values, attitudes and behaviours. Values that are held but never expressed by senior clinicians are not adequately conveyed to young people and newcomers (Reynolds 1994). Society expects the provision of healthcare to reflect its values, but resources are not made available within the organisation for these to be put into practice. Unless these issues are addressed, society will continue to get the doctors it deserves rather than the doctors it professes to want.

Quality improvement in healthcare is not just about improving the treatment of patients. It is also about ensuring that healthcare organisations and the professionals who work within them reflect the values of society and ensure that future generations are educated in these values and attitudes, as well as in required clinical knowledge

Table 5.1 Continuing Medical Education (CME) and Continuing Professional Development (CPD)

CME	*CPD*
• vocational	professional
• about clinical skills/knowledge	more than clinical knowledge/skills
• keeping clinical knowledge up to date	includes management, education/ training issues, clinical governance
• starts after formal education ends	ongoing personal development and improvement
• limited in scope	extends/affirms professional values

and skills. The Hippocratic oath acknowledged the dual responsibilities of the physician to both education and patient care. 'I will keep this Oath ... to reckon him who taught me this Art equally dear to me as my parents ... to look upon his offspring on the same footing as my own brothers, and to teach them this art ... by precept, lecture and by every other mode of instruction, I will impart a knowledge of the art to my own sons ... I will follow that system or regimen which, according to my ability and judgement, I consider for the benefit of my patients...'. To the patient before them our predecessors offered care and advice; to those to come they offered the education of the next generation of physicians. Care and education were inextricably bound – the one ensuring that those requiring help and support received it; the other that values, knowledge and skills were refined, developed and shared with the generation to follow.

This chapter is about ensuring that education in the attitudes, values, skills and knowledge of ethical medical professionalism which are essential for good patient care and for the implementation of clinical governance, are embedded within systems of healthcare provision. Such education needs to be sufficiently robust to enable healthcare organisations to contend with the challenges of technology, political pressures, changing demography and relentlessly increasing workload. Only by doing so can the quality of patient services ultimately be secured. While this review will concentrate on the education of medical professionals, its observations on the fundamental importance of a value system reflecting societal and professional views of healthcare are appropriate for all clinical groups.

The role of society and healthcare institutions

Medical professionalism is a set of values, attitudes and behaviours that results in serving the interests of patients and society before one's own (Reynolds 1994). Increasingly, however, the public expects to have a say in what represents their best interests. Society must recognise the challenges of new technologies and the ethical dilemmas raised by them; an ageing and increasingly multi-cultural population with ever greater expectations of, and demands for, healthcare, and a political environment characterised by change (Abelson *et al.* 1997). The values society develops in response to these are reflected in many aspects of life, including healthcare. If healthcare is to embody the values of society rather than simply those of the medical profession, then the public must be prepared to make those values explicit and to provide the resources necessary for them to be reflected in practice.

Each healthcare organisation must take cognisance of the values of its local community and ensure that the education of its professional groups safeguards and develops them. Chief executives of healthcare organisations increasingly recognise this accountability to the values of their local community (Heard 1997). The continuing professional development of clinicians who are responsible for the education and training of those to follow must reflect these values, for example, effective team-working, and ensure they are embedded in the knowledge, skills and attitudes of those they train.

Selecting students for tomorrow's service

Society depends on medical schools to select students with the intellect and the personality to become tomorrow's doctors: the self-improving, collaborative and caring medical staff needed for a modern health service. The caring physician has the ability to project his or herself into the patient's position or state of mind, thus becoming sensitive to signs of stress, emotional disturbances, and expressions of pain and to appreciate feelings, tendencies, and intentions as well (Scott *et al.* 1995). Medical schools have struggled without much success to find ways of identifying these attributes in young people attracted to medicine. Most recognise that academic excellence alone is not enough, but end up selecting on the basis of academic results for want of better measures (McManus 1997). Given the scientific basis of medicine, it is not surprising that they also favour candidates with a record of achievement in science subjects, despite evidence that schoolboy science specialists are more likely to approve of social conformity, to be more authoritarian and to display more violence and cruelty than their arts counterparts (Hudson 1974). Doctors tend to select in their own image. If the public has responsibility for determining the kind of healthcare it wants and the values it wishes embodied, then it should also have a say in how its future doctors are chosen (Collier 1997).

When the Council of Deans of Medical Schools in Britain recommended a move away from purely academic means of selecting students, the move was welcomed in the lay press: 'The arrogance displayed in recent medical negligence cases is part of a culture which views patients as intellectual problems, rather than as people. Any moves like the Deans', are welcome moves to attack this problem at the root.' (*The Independent*, editorial, 1998).

Passing through the mirror

In a remarkable in-depth study of basic medical training in a London teaching hospital, Sinclair (1997) observed how students learned a new way of seeing the world 'first through its scientising and then its pathologising'. As they experienced this paradigm shift, they aligned themselves increasingly with their colleagues and seniors in the profession and distanced themselves from non-medical friends and the world of their patients. As Hughes (1984) has put it, 'one might say that the learning of the medical role consists of a separation, almost an alienation, of the student from the lay medical world, a passing through the mirror so that one looks out on the world from behind it, and sees things in mirror writing.' Intense personal idealism gives way to professional idealism, with patients valued for the clinical experience they offer or their co-operation with the medical agenda.

This process is probably inevitable as the student learns to behave in a controlled professional manner, in the face of the horrors of disease, trauma and human tragedy, but it is not without price in the development of the caring physician. Nor did seeing the world through the mirror necessarily offer a solution to the stresses inherent in the profession. 'Many students appeared unable to attend to social and political aspects of relationships, and be untouched by social constraints and struggles and, generally, unaware of the reasons for their distress.' (Sinclair 1997). Students appeared to be unaware of their own internal conflict, and to have adopted the cultural aversion to investigating social and psychological matters that pervade much of the profession. Whether the reforms to the undergraduate curriculum recommended by the General Medical Council will alter the situation described, and will foster the development of the caring physician remains to be seen (General Medical Council 1993).

Tough transitions

There is a world of difference between being a medical student, responsible only for oneself, and being a doctor with all the burdens that the word implies. It is vital for a quality service that the new doctor acquires the attributes of a caring physician in making these transitions. Unfortunately, the healthcare organisation itself may provide barriers to this. Too often the economic pressures of the organisation prevent the new doctor from having control over their work or time for appropriate communication or reflection. The desirable qualities of empathy and self-criticism then lead to disillusionment and depression (Firth-Cozens 1992). In these circumstances, coping strategies are developed which may become ingrained, the foremost of which is personal detachment. The General Medical Council has published recommendations on improving the pre-registration year, which, if successfully implemented, should improve both quality of training and quality of patient care (General Medical Council 1997). There is a clear emphasis on such professional values as teamwork, advancing medical knowledge, good communication, using evidence and critical appraisal in making decisions, appropriate working in a multi-cultural environment and developing a holistic approach to patient care. The educational approach required to secure learning in these areas is set out and healthcare organisations are given a clear responsibility to ensure that systems and resources are in place to enable this learning to take place.

It will hardly come as a surprise to note that these recommendations reflect the values and principles contained within the GMC's *Good Medical Practice* (General Medical Council 1995). The 14 principles enunciated in that document modernise and clarify the values of the medical profession originally laid out by Hippocrates. They set the context for doctors who are about to take up full registration and are the basis upon which on-going registration of medical practice will rest for the entirety of a practitioner's working life (General Medical Council 2000). Indeed, since these principles are so fundamental to the ethos of being a doctor, it may be that in the selection of applicants to medical schools, exploration of a candidate's values and their views of *Good Medical Practice* should be a mandatory part of the process of admission.

Organisational barriers to learning

In common with many other professions, including the clergy and the armed forces, medicine is experiencing a generational change in the attitudes of its newer recruits (Paice 1997). Young doctors are increasingly eager to have a life outside medicine (Allen 1997), and, while this may be especially true for the growing number of women doctors, it is a feeling shared by their male colleagues. Working hours of junior doctors in Britain have recently been reduced in response to increasing evidence that long hours impair the health of doctors as well as the quality of patient care. Unfortunately the health service, chronically under-supplied with doctors, depends on junior doctors to cover the hospital at night and at the weekend. Attempts to maintain traditional working patterns within reduced hours have led to intolerable intensity of work, while the introduction of shift-work has proved destructive to social life, continuity of patient care, and continuity of education and training (Baldwin *et al.* 1997). Junior doctors now spend less time in the company of their peers or working under the direct supervision of their consultant trainers, because a greater proportion of their working week is spent providing out of hours cover. Senior doctors, already pressured by increasing patient expectations and their own growing workload, feel they now have to pick up more work as their juniors clock off. It doesn't help that they themselves may be suffering from the relationship consequences of years of working long hours. The consultants become distanced from, and out of sympathy with, their trainees and an important supportive quasi-paternal relationship is eroded (Hale & Hudson 1992). Factors that alleviate stress – having a sense of control over one's work, experiencing group support, having opportunities to use one's skills, and gaining feedback on the value of one's role – are less likely to be enjoyed by either party. Doctors in training are more likely to fall back on the coping strategy of increasing personal detachment (Scott *et al.* 1995).

The quality of the service context in which a trainee works determines to a large extent the quality of the training. Equally, the quality of training determines the quality of service that the trainee is able to offer, both now, and in the future. The most important determinant of quality training in the hospital context is the quality of consultant supervision, both clinical and educational (Paice 1998). Unfortunately, reforms to postgraduate medical education have not taken into account the additional burden they would place on consultants (Royal College of Physicians 1998). Resources have not been made available in terms of time or extra staff. The consequence is an increasing division of labour, with trainees carrying out many of their tasks separate from the consultant trainer.

Healthcare organisations need to reconsider education within this context and with the recognition that the way in which patient care is currently delivered is significantly different from ten years ago. Reduced lengths of inpatient stay, one-stop clinics, day surgery and more care delivered out of hospital in the community, require innovative approaches to education that both reflect the context of these changes, work within them and enable doctors in training to adjust to them.

Learn together, work together

One solution to the doctors' dilemma of balancing the need for a personal life with the need to offer continuity of patient care is to develop team working in which responsibility for continuity of care is carried by the team, not by individuals. More and more, modern healthcare is being delivered by multi-disciplinary teams. Quality is best assured where care is provided by multidisciplinary teams, with shared goals, clear individual roles, strong leadership and a clear sense of direction. Learning as a team ensures that the learning is put into action and that team members reinforce rather than obstruct innovation.

The General Medical Council considers being able to work in a team an essential part of good medical practice.

> To be effective, medical and clinical teams must be well led and managed. They must:
>
> - have a positive attitude to patients and listen to their wishes and needs;
> - make themselves aware of what patients think about the quality of their services;
> - and have a clear understanding of their professional values, standards and purpose.
>
> (General Medical Council 1998)

Unfortunately, doctors are not well prepared for working in teams with other professionals. Their education and training for this role is rarely given sufficient attention. Those drawn to medicine are people with a strong need to work autonomously. They do not have the background of teamwork, collaboration, and empowering other people (Smith 1992). Medical students form negative views of the status of specialties where responsibility is shared with other professional groups (Sinclair 1997). Education for effective teamwork is not something that can be relegated to the undergraduate curriculum, but must be a part of the lifelong learning of all doctors, whatever their seniority.

Educating towards clinical governance

The recent White Paper issued by Britain's Labour Government has linked managerial accountability to the quality of clinical service through the concept of clinical governance (Department of Health 1997). The intention presumably was to address the widespread perception that health service managers are interested primarily in the financial bottom line, while clinicians are trained to pursue clinical quality without regard to cost implications. Clinical governance requires the organisation to demonstrate that the systems and processes are in place to ensure consistent quality of service. The definition and measures of clinical quality will require an explicit examination of the values of the institution, the local community it serves, and the wider NHS as indicated by the 'Ten Cs' of Clinicial Governance (Heard 1998):

1. core values
2. committed leadership
3. clear accountability
4. culture of clinical excellence
5. continuing education/professional development
6. clinical audit
7. complaints management
8. clinical risk management
9. continuing health needs assessment
10. changing practice through evidence.

Junior doctors, moving from hospital to hospital in the course of their training, are potentially a weak point in the system of clinical governance. Their interests and their loyalties lie outside the organisations they work in. As front-line workers they are often given the onus of implementing clinical guidelines, a contributory factor in the failure of guidelines to work (McNicol *et al.* 1993). Clinical audit is another area where success has depended excessively on the participation of doctors in training without due attention to educational principles. In a study of junior doctors' perceptions of clinical audit meetings, it was clear that trainees felt threatened and blamed for any identified deficiencies in care. Trainees therefore became increasingly reluctant to bring material for discussion. The atmosphere was combative and confrontational, so that mistakes tended to be covered up rather than discussed (Firth-Cozens & Storer 1992).

So how can the healthcare organisation engage junior doctors in its clinical governance agenda? One strategy may be to develop a curriculum to cover the knowledge, skills and attitudes required to deliver clinical governance in any specialty, any healthcare profession or any institution. Such an approach would acknowledge that professional development does not start when formal clinical training ends, but that understanding the values and developing these alongside of clinical skills is every bit as important as achieving exams and specialty knowledge. This generic curriculum could be agreed by, and delivered in, a range of institutions linked by training rotations or other common interests. Delivered in the workplace, and shared by all healthcare professionals, it would have the potential to develop the mutual respect, understanding and shared goals that underpin successful teamwork. It would provide a forum for open discussion amongst all the members of the clinical and managerial team. It would ensure that trainees are prepared for full and active participation in pursuing quality improvement both during their remaining training and when they achieve a career post.

A suggested regional curriculum is set out in the case study in Table 5.2 (Heard 2000). It has pre-empted the direction of education and workforce development indicated by the consultation paper *A Health Service of all the Talents: developing the NHS Workforce* (Department of Health 2000). Developed through a jointly funded initiative involving the eight educational consortia and the postgraduate deans in North Thames, the educational aims and learning objectives of the curriculum were agreed and have now been implemented through local, consortium-based educational programmes across the patch. Two hundred and eleven participants have received training in one or more of three modules on offer and completed evaluations of these. Feedback has been extremely positive with: 92 per cent of participants responding, indicating that it enhanced their understanding of clinical governance; 96 per cent noting that it is likely to enhance multi-professional working in a current/future team; 99 per cent claiming that it is likely to impact on clinical performance to the benefit of patient care; and 99 per cent stating that they would recommend the educational programme to a colleague.

Conclusions: educating for the future

How do we ensure that this ethical framework informs medical education; that future doctors underpin their scientific decision-making with humanity, humility and ideals of public service; that they offer not just the right clinical answers but respond to patients within a quality framework of integrity and accountability? There is little doubt that senior healthcare professionals are key in providing appropriate models of behaviour, of mentoring trainees and of setting and expecting standards of practice reflecting high quality performance.

The demands on all healthcare professionals are so numerous and varied that sometimes the focus and purpose of what we do are lost. However the focus in

Table 5.2 Case study

	Managing life in the NHS: educating towards clinical governance
Aim:	to devise and implement a curriculum to develop the core values necessary to work within the new NHS in support of clinical governance and improved patient care
Principles:	to be delivered in multi-professional groups, in the workplace and across the patch
Method:	a Steering Group was established including nurses, midwives and professions allied to medicine, a senior medical trainee representative, a dental postgraduate dean and a trust medical director. Facilitation for the group was provided by the regional educational advisor. The group met to agree the curriculum, its modular components and the constituents of these; to develop a system of quality control and an evaluation strategy. Wide consultation on the curriculum across NHS organisations and professional groups was subsequently undertaken prior to implementation of the educational programme.
Curriculum:	
	Module 1: Knowledge
	1. Clinical governance and the modern NHS 2. Quality, complaints and clinical risk management in the NHS 3. Critical analysis of data and evidence and its use in making clinical decisions 4. Diversity and equal opportunities for staff and patients 5. Managing financial resources
	Module 2: Skills
	1. Presentation skills and managing meetings 2. Clinical audit skills 3. Managing life during change, leadership and working in teams 4. Negotiation and conflict 5. Appraisal and performance management
	Module 3: Attitudes and personal development
	1. Communicating with patients and colleagues 2. Assertiveness and influence 3. Time management and prioritising 4. Career development – the next stages 5. Mentoring, supervision and supporting colleagues

medicine must always be clear – it is not the technology or the pushing back of scientific boundaries, nor the interests of the specialty, profession or institution we work in; the focus is the patient, today and in the future. healthcare professionals have the responsibility, and the privilege, of helping the patient to identify their needs and within the shared framework of society's ethical framework, offering the support needed.

Training and education for a responsive, self-critical and constantly improving service requires an educational environment that encourages open discussion of problems. We need to identify, support and reward the master clinician-teachers who can act as role models both for teaching and for practice. 'Learning excellence in patient care requires superb clinical role models who uphold the patient as a person and who show that being a physician demands dedication to patient care and continuous learning over one's lifetime.' (Reynolds 1994). Above all, it requires time: time for communication between carers and patients, managers and clinicians, trainers and trainees. It also requires time for all healthcare professionals to think about what they are doing, to reflect on their own performance and to invigorate and energise their practice through this reflection. Clinical governance, education and lifelong professional development are not optional extras – they are the heart and life-blood of quality in clinical care.

References

Abelson J, Maxwell PH, Maxwell RJ (1997). Do professions have a future? *British Medical Journal* **315**, 382

Allen I (1997). What doctors want from their careers. In Allen I, Brown P, Hughes P (eds) *Choosing Tomorrow's Doctors.* London: Policy Studies Institute

Baldwin PJ, Newton RW, Buckley G, Roberts MA, Dodds M (1997). Senior house officers in medicine: a postal survey of training and work experience. *British Medical Journal* **314**, 740–743

Collier J (1997). Ethical issues in the selection of medical students. In Allen I, Brown P, Hughes P (eds) *Choosing Tomorrow's Doctors.* London: Policy Studies Institute

Department of Health (1998). *A First Class Service: Quality in the New NHS.* London: HMSO

Department of Health (2000). *A Health Service of all the Talents: Developing the NHS Workforce.* London: HMSO

Department of Health (1997). *The New NHS: Modern/Dependable.* London: HMSO

Firth-Cozens J (1992). The role of early family experiences in the perception of organisational stress: fusing clinical and organisational perspectives. *Journal of Occupational and Organisational Psychology* **65**, 61–75

Firth-Cozens J & Storer D (1992). Registrars' and senior registrars' perceptions of their audit activities, *Quality in Healthcare* **1**, 161–164

General Medical Council (1995). *Good Medical Practice.* London: GMC

General Medical Council (1998). *Maintaining Good Medical Practice.* London: GMC

General Medical Council (2000). *Revalidation Consultation.* London: GMC

General Medical Council (1997). *The New Doctor: Recommendations on General Clinical Training.* London: GMC

General Medical Council (1993). *Tomorrow's Doctors: Recommendations on Undergraduate Medical Education*. London: GMC

Hale R & Hudson L (1992). The Tavistock Study of Young Doctors: report of the pilot phase. *British Journal of Hospital Medicine* **47**, 452–464

Heard SR (1998). Educating for clinical governance. *Hospital Medicine* **59**, 728–729

Heard SR (2000). Management development for clinicians: a personal perspective from a postgraduate dean. *Clinician in Management* **9**, 1–4

Heard SR (1997). Quality healthcare: the hospital's chief executive role. *Quality in Healthcare* **2**, 99–101

Hudson L (1974). *Contrary Imaginations: a Psychological Study of the English Schoolboy*. London: Penguin

Hughes E (1984). *The Sociological Eye*. New Jersey: New Brunswick Transaction

McManus C (1997). From selection to qualification: how and why medical students change. In Allen I, Brown P, Hughes P (eds) *Choosing Tomorrow's Doctors*. London: Policy Studies Institute

McNicol M, Layton A, Morgan G (1993). Team-working: the key to implementing Guidelines. *Quality in Healthcare* **2**, 215–6

Paice E (1997). Why young doctors leave the profession. *Journal of the Royal Society of Medicine* **90**, 417–418

Paice E (1998). Is the new deal compatible with good senior house officer training? *Hospital Medicine* **59**, 72–74

Reynolds PP (1994). Reaffirming professionalism through the education community. *Annals of Internal Medicine* **120**, 609–614

Royal College of Physicians (1998). Coping with pressures in acute medicine. The Royal College of Physicians Consultant Questionnaire Survey. *Journal of the Royal College of Physicians of London* **32**, 211–218

Scott RA, Aiken LH, Mechanic D, Moravcsik J (1995). Organizational aspects of caring. *The Millbank Quarterly* **73**, 77–95

Sinclair S (1997). *Making Doctors: An Institutional Apprenticeship*. Oxford

Smith R (1992). Leadership and doctors. *British Medical Journal* **3**, 137–138

Chapter 6

Measuring clinical governance: endpoints that are clinically relevant and organisationally meaningful

Philippa Hewer and Myriam Lugon

With the publication of the Government's White Paper *The New NHS. Modern Dependable* (Department of Health 1997), the quality of clinical care has been brought to the top of the agenda and the concept of clinical governance introduced. Not only will chief executives have responsibility for the financial health of the organisation, but they will also have a duty with regard to clinical quality (Department of Health 1998). All areas of healthcare now need to progress with the implementation of clinical governance, the elements of which were outlined in a health service circular – *Clinical Governance: in the New NHS* (Department of Health 1999a). Clinical governance gives a focus to the activity of the organisations and its clinical staff so that high standards of care, in line with published best practice, are delivered consistently. The definition of clinical governance as published in the circular is:

> ... a framework through which NHS organisations are accountable for continuously improving the quality of their services and safeguarding high standards of care by creating an environment in which excellence in clinical care will flourish.
>
> (Department of Health 1998)

This should be about ensuring the patient's journey is good and about learning from their experience to deliver services that better meet the needs of patients. It is also about ownership by clinical teams and support from the organisation to deliver optimal care. In order to achieve this, all quality initiatives must be linked and adequate processes and systems put in place to capture the care process.

What is the responsibility of the organisation?

The organisation needs to create an environment which promotes learning and teamwork, in which clinical teams feel empowered to reflect on their practice and implement changes. Organisations can put in place a number of structures, activities and people to help develop care and facilitate the measurement of the quality of care. In particular, support is needed to undertake work around patients and users of services, routinely to evaluate their experiences of care and involve them in developing services. Leadership is another pre-requisite for success, with champions to lead the implementation process and develop measurable outcomes. Champions alone are not sufficient and organisational support is essential in taking forward change, both in the form of a relevant and useful committee structure, necessary to monitor progress with implementation (Lugon & Secker-Walker 1999) and in access to individuals skilled in supporting clinical and non-clinical staff in the 'technical' aspects of clinical governance. These individuals need to be able to design projects, to find and appraise evidence and act as facilitators for the different teams and professionals. Using standard tools across the organisation, such as a framework for developing an action plan and monitoring progress through the achievement of particular end points, will enable progress reports to be made and ensure consistency of approach across the organisation.

Ensuring consistency in approach

The organisation needs to offer leadership in the implementation of clinical governance and make clear to its clinical teams the goals they need to achieve. The development of a framework against which to assess the current state of affairs and measure progress should allow clinical teams to identify the priorities for action in a consistent way. By understanding what needs to be achieved, clinical teams will be better placed to develop an action plan with leads and timescale that will guide the activities for the year. The action plan should describe specific topics, the activities to be undertaken, the names of lead people and timescales agreed for achieving measurable outcomes. These may be related to processes such as identifying key people for clinical risk management, planning and delivering training or improving specific health outcomes. These endpoints need to be both pertinent to the issue identified and a valid measure in relation to the activities undertaken. The framework is intended, in this example, to be used by multidisciplinary clinical improvement groups (CIGs) (Burke & Lugon 1998) set up within each directorate, for the purpose of implementing clinical governance.

This particular framework for clinical governance activities within an organisation has been developed to focus thinking on the key components and tasks of clinical governance; to identify where each service is currently placed and what needs to be done to achieve the aims and objectives set by the organisation; to compare progress made by different parts of an organisation and share good practice. It allows for the development of short- to medium-term objectives for individuals, teams and directorates which will contribute to the achievement of the overall aims of clinical governance.

An important element of the framework is the measurement of improvement over time. In the past, organisations worked with a number of quality initiatives, which in many cases were not complementary and very few adopted a systematic approach to measuring results. In a number of cases, the measurement of the delivery of care frequently used endpoints which were not identified or agreed by clinical teams as being relevant in their situation. Involving all stakeholders in the identification and collection of data increases the effect of this information in improving care. The purpose of the framework is to ensure that the organisation sustains improvements already made, and moves forward in the context of clearly defined service aims and objectives.

The aims of the framework are:

1. To share the vision of what the organisation is aiming to achieve with regard to clinical governance, based on the organisation's purpose, aims and values.
2. To identify key strategic clinical governance objectives which are the same for all levels of the organisation, including teams and individuals.
3. To communicate these objectives in a way that is understandable to staff, so that they can be aware of how their individual work contributes to the success of the organisation.
4. To develop a structured system to measure the current position in relation to the clinical governance objectives, in order to facilitate planning and monitoring over time.

The framework is designed to identify key result areas needing to be achieved to ensure that exceptions are identified and managed, services provided are clinically effective, staff are developed and empowered and that 'open management' is provided. The key results areas cover clinical risk and complaints management, clinical audit and clinical effectiveness, processes for implementation of national service frameworks (NSFs) and NICE guidance, workforce planning, education and training and procedures to monitor performance. In each a number of endpoints that are clinically and/or organisationally meaningful are identified, so these indicators allow progress to be measured easily (Lugon & Secker-Walker 2001). These endpoints are clearly stated and can be achieved across the various parts of an organisation.

An action plan for the implementation of each subsection is agreed with each directorate and the relevant central co-ordinating committee. The plan specifies the key tasks, systems and processes that are to be established during a specific time period. It is recognised that many services will already have established many governance systems and, as such, each plan is customised to individual service development needs. However certain corporate tasks and timescales are mandatory and all actions plans are expected to include these.

How is this agenda taken forward?

Delivering care and giving attention to quality is a team effort. Within the organisation, clinical improvement groups (CIGs), or their equivalent, should be charged with the task of progressing the agenda at clinical team level and developing ownership and commitment of the clinical governance agenda.

Such groups should be multidisciplinary, directorate- or department-based and made up of senior clinicians and managers (Burke & Lugon 1998). Their role is to review available information with the aim of managing risks and improving care through a structured process, as shown in Figure 6.1.

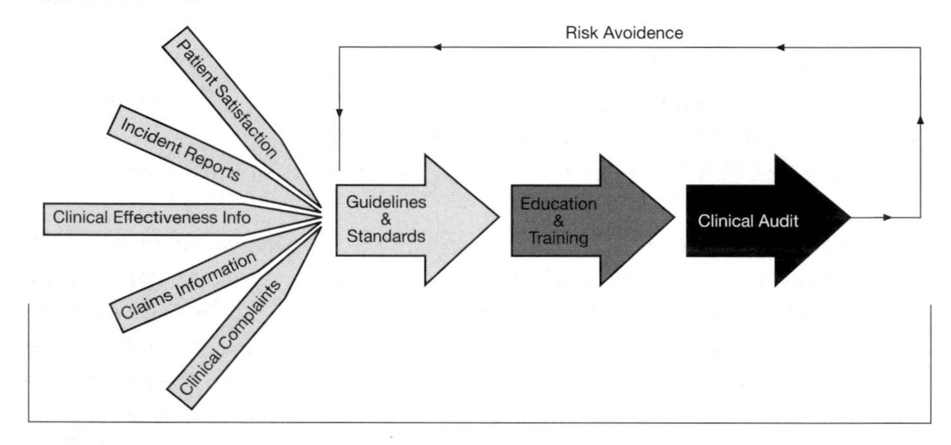

Figure 6.1 Toward clinical improvement. Reproduced with permission from Burke C and Lugon M © HRRI

Through reviewing information about incidents, complaints, claims and patient satisfaction and combining this with examples of best practice, such as research evidence, guidance from the National Institute for Clinical Excellence (NICE) and other sources, guidelines may be developed and standards for practice agreed and implemented. Implementing this into practice and the results of subsequent audit will quantify the effects of these changes and the achievement of standards, providing realistic endpoints. The measurement of the quality of care can then be fed back and appropriate actions taken as part of an updated clinical governance action plan relating to the areas identified in the framework. This approach aims primarily at avoiding risk and improving the quality of clinical care, consistent with the principles of clinical governance.

The 'technical' aspects of clinical governance

Clinical governance covers a number of specific areas, where the presence of clear structures and processes contributes to supporting the delivery of high quality care. Progressing this agenda requires a set of indicators that can be easily measured and are credible to clinical staff. Initially, these indicators are mainly ones relating to processes, while services are asked to identify outcome measures of care within their particular areas. The areas described below all form part of the framework and are linked to the development of the action plan.

Clinical audit

Clinical audit must be accepted as a valid tool to provide information about where changes in clinical practice or service delivery need to occur (Burke & Lugon 1999). It is thus the responsibility of the whole clinical and managerial team. The audit programme needs to address the areas where there is a question about a particular aspect of care. It needs to be informed by qualitative (complaints, incidents, claims etc.) and quantitative (clinical indicators, mortality rate etc.) information made available to the team. Each of these areas will describe possible endpoints, such as the targets specified in the national service frameworks or the outcomes of investigations into clinical incidents.

The methodology must be sound and practice measured against known evidence-based clinical standards (Miles *et al.* 1996). Standard setting should include relevant clinical indicators, covering both the process and outcomes of care. These should also be meaningful to the organisation, in relation to aspects of quality and resource usage. In order to facilitate change as a result of audit the data collected need to be credible to those individuals required to change their practice. Recommendations identified as a result of the audit activities need to result in measurable changes. These recommendations should be clear, measurable, and be achieved within an agreed timescale. To encourage changes as the result of audit, this process should be multi disciplinary, reflecting the priorities and perceptions of healthcare professionals, managers, patients and carers. In addition, providing feedback to all staff within the team and other stakeholders about the results of audit and the reasons for changing practice helps complete the loop and encourage continuing improvements in practice.

The research evidence of the effectiveness of prompt thrombolytic therapy for patients with myocardial infarction (MI) is included in the standards set within the *National Service Framework for Coronary Heart Disease* (Department of Health 2000). This provides a number of indicators for the delivery of high quality care, including that of the time elapsed between the patient arriving in the accident and emergency department and receiving thrombolytic therapy. In addition to this process measure, the incidence of death following MI will be used as an outcome measure to assess the effects of care over time.

Risk management

The organisation should have a written clinical risk management policy identifying the roles and responsibilities from the chief executive to the individual within a clinical team (Lugon 1996; Secker-Walker 1999). This needs to be translated into a clinical risk management procedure at service level. The key elements are shown in Table 6.1.

For this to be done effectively, the organisational culture must be a non-punitive and supportive one. It is only in this climate that incidents will be identified and reported as they occur. Risk management should be co-ordinated within each clinical service and incidents investigated so that appropriate managerial action can be taken to prevent the repetition of a similar event whenever possible. The information generated by incident reporting should be given to clinical teams on a regular basis so that they can reflect on trends and identify areas where either clinical or managerial practice needs to be reviewed. Serious clinical incidents need to be thoroughly investigated and clear recommendations agreed. Recommendations from two fictitious examples are given in Table 6.2. The appropriate committee should monitor progress with the implementation of these recommendations carefully.

Table 6.1 Key components of clinical risk management programme.

- A written explicit clinical risk management procedure, including serious clinical incidents
- Dissemination and training to support the use of this policy
- Identification of speciality specific 'trigger events' – a list of incidents which can be collated under defined categories
- Incidents are reported, investigated and lessons learnt
- Risk assessments are undertaken, with actions as a result of this
- Inclusion of infection control, health and safety and other related incidents
- Training and support available to all staff
- Inclusion on the induction programme.

Table 6.2 Fictitious example of serious incident recommendations

	Issue	*Recommendations*	*Lead*	*Date*	*Progress*
SCI 1	Misdiagnosis of gastric bleed due to oesophageal varices	Include diagnosis and treatment in compulsory teaching sessions of SHO	Clinical director A&E	Nov 2000	Scheduled for Wed Oct 10th
SCI 2	Availability of specialist opinion out of hours	Contact out of hours to be circulated to all juniors	Clinical director Ophthalmology	September 2000	Done

Compliance with statutory requirements such as those relating to health and safety and control of infection will also need to be monitored. Other indicators, which provide measurable endpoints, include actions such as the inclusion of risk management in the induction programme and availability of training for the clinical team.

Information

Without accurate, relevant and timely information, the quality of care cannot be monitored and service delivery reviewed and improved. The measurement and demonstration of the quality of care is a key feature of clinical governance. A large amount of data is collected within the NHS, with a number of acknowledged problems with data quality, coding and timeliness. Agreeing the definition of clinically relevant endpoints and implementing this into existing IT systems is often a long and frustrating task. National initiatives, such as information for health (Department of Health 1999b) and the development of local implementation strategies should encourage greater consistency of approach and increase the inclusion of relevant clinical information. However, clinical teams need to identify what information will help them monitor process and outcome of care and discuss this with their IM&T department so as to receive this information regularly in a form that facilitates its use. The content of clinical complaints, claims and clinical incidents should form part of this package of information on which action will be taken.

For example, an accident and emergency department may review information relating to waiting times for admission, using information from computer systems used for monitoring Patient's Charter standards, and cross reference this with complaints and incidents reported by staff, to both prioritise areas for work and evaluate the effects of changes in practice. In mental health services, the review of information relating to readmission from a number of sources (IM&T, incidents, complaints, user and staff views) may help identify areas for future action in relation to improving the quality of services.

Clinical effectiveness

Research, particularly into clinically important and relevant questions, forms the basis of evidence-based practice (Haines *et al.* 1996). While all individuals within a clinical team will not undertake research, the implementation of research findings should be part of everyone's business. Evidence-based information should thus be disseminated appropriately within the team and inform the clinical quality improvement programme. Clinical audit should be used as a tool to identify how far current practice differs from agreed best practice and so help monitor implementation of the improvements required. Not everything in medicine and healthcare generally has clear-cut evidence, therefore training staff in search strategies and critical appraisal is an important element of the effectiveness agenda.

Training and development

To provide high quality care, staff need to be appropriately skilled and ensure that these skills are maintained through appropriate training (Weight *et al.* 1999). Within a clinical team, staff should be clear about the competencies and experience required to do the work effectively and efficiently. Training attended by staff should be monitored, and a personal development plan agreed on a yearly basis with individual members of the team at their review of performance. Training should be multidisciplinary whenever possible, such as resuscitation training, complaints, clinical risk management, health and safety, control of infection etc. Directorate training plans can be developed from individual training plans and integrated with the action plan for clinical governance. Clear standards for clinical practice will determine the skills and competencies needed within a clinical team. Various means (clinical supervision, appraisal etc.) will then be used to identify where shortfalls exist so that the appropriate training and development programme can be put in place. The effect of training and development can then be measured using tools such as clinical audit, where appropriate, clinical supervision, mentoring etc.

Patient feedback

The aspects of quality and clinical governance perceived by patients (Sweeney 2000) and other users of services will differ in some respects from those identified by clinical staff. Complaints give an individual story that can point to an area where clinical and/or managerial practice could be improved (Hobbs 1999; Lugon in press). Indicators should therefore include how complaints are dealt with and in what timescale, whether the complaints are reviewed by the clinical team so that trends inform changes, whether recommendations from independent review panels are considered and implemented, whether staff in the directorate have been trained in complaints handling and what means are used by the directorate pro-actively to seek patient feedback so as to improve service delivery.

Over time, less attention has been directed to this crucial aspect of care and it has been somewhat neglected. throughout the development of clinical quality improvement initiatives within the NHS. Although a number of publications (Kelson 1998, 1999) have clearly outlined the way in which this might take place, and the benefits of involving patients, users and carers in clinical quality improvement activities, there are still few examples of this in practice.

In learning from patients, their experiences, feelings and opinions provide a measure of how well their needs and expectations were met. Defining endpoints relevant to patients prior to patients experiencing the service, clarifies the aims and objectives from a consumer's point of view (Davis 2000).

This process can also be used to engage patients, clients, relatives and carers in service design and delivery, with the potential to reduce complaints and claims in the longer term. In the shorter term, consideration of the user perspective and feeding their comments back into the delivery of care increases the responsiveness of services.

Monitoring progress with the clinical governance agenda

Monitoring progress and identifying problems with care in a structured way increases confidence in clinical governance as an appropriate vehicle for clinical quality improvement. Developing and monitoring a clear plan of action reduces uncertainty, confusion and an underlying feeling that none of it makes any real difference. Agreeing achievable targets, given resource constraints and the capacity of groups to take on more work, helps to focus activities in the most worthwhile areas. Supporting this with clear organisational structures, technical support staff and communicating the aims and objectives to all staff promotes its implementation and indicates the commitment of the organisation to these activities. Training will be required in a number of areas, but can be targeted well as a result of having clear roles and responsibilities. Indicators to monitor progress enable successes to be acknowledged and problems identified at an early stage. The involvement of patients in drafting and agreeing this plan is crucial, as is the development of patient-relevant endpoints as indicators.

The clinical governance improvement plan for the organisation will be developed alongside the use of a framework to establish the current situation and indicate work required to improve the situation.

What are the challenges with regard to implementation?

Gaining ownership from multidisciplinary clinical teams around the clinical governance agenda is a challenge in the NHS. Clinical teams are not all cohesive and professional boundaries are often difficult to cross. Teams which are functioning well and have clearly identified individuals and group responsibilities, will find this easier than other, less well-functioning, teams. The existence of a clear agenda for change and commitment to this throughout the multi disciplinary team will encourage participation. A culture change is required not only for the grass roots but also for the corporate functions in the organisation. Quality must be considered on a par with finance and activity and become a priority for the board. With the many conflicting initiatives, little time is left to reflect and learn.

Evolution not revolution

The process of implementing clinical governance is a long one, with a need to identify progress at all stages, in addition to demonstrating the quality of care. It is an extensive agenda, integrated into every aspect of healthcare planning and delivery. The development of robust endpoints will enable not only the demonstration of the quality of care, but will facilitate benchmarking across organisations and raise awareness of the issues facing the NHS. Increased information about healthcare, the decision making, the management of risk and so on, can only improve outcomes and expectations. Clinically relevant and organisationally meaningful end points will move this agenda forward in a clear and systematic way.

Do we need incentives?

Any incentives should be taken in the context of the time and resources available. Publicising good practice, disseminating it throughout the organisation and outside the immediate locality can encourage others to follow in the footsteps of the high achievers. Instituting a clinical quality improvement award could also encourage individuals and teams to continue the good work done. In the end, time will need to be made available for clinical teams to reflect and learn from what they do. This needs to become an integral part of the business of the clinical team. Only when quality improvement is truly integrated into day-to-day business, will this agenda be successful and patient care consistently improved.

References

Burke C & Lugon M (1998). Integrating clinical risk and audit – moving towards clinical governance. *The Health Risk Resource* **1**, 16–18

Burke C & Lugon M (1999). Clinical audit and clinical governance. In Lugon M & Secker-Walker J (eds) *Clinical Governance. Making it Happen*. London: RSM Press, pp 61–76

Davis J (2000). Harnessing patient involvement – the challenges in determining patient satisfaction. *Clinical Governance Bulletin* **1**, 10–11

Department of Health (1997). *The New NHS. Modern Dependable*. London: HMSO

Department of Health (1998). *A First Class Service. Quality in the New NHS*. London: HMSO

Department of Health (1999a). *Clinical Governance: in the New NHS*. London: HMSO

Department of Health (1999b). *Information for Health*. London: HMSO

Department of Health (2000). *National Service Framework for Coronary Heart Disease*. London: HMSO

Haines A, Freemantle N, Watt I, Lugon M (1996). Increasing the effectiveness of clinical intervention. In Miles A & Lugon M (eds) *Effective Clinical Practice*. Oxford: Blackwell Science, pp124–143

Hobbs S (1999). Learning from complaints. In Lugon M & Secker-Walker J (eds) *Clinical Governance. Making it Happen*. London: RSM Press, pp177–130.

Kelson M (1998). *Promoting Patient Involvement in Clinical Audit. Practical Guidance on Achieving Effective Involvement.* College of Health

Kelson M (1999). *Patient-Defined Outcomes.* College of Health

Lugon M (1996). Developing a trust clinical risk management policy and procedure. *Clinical Risk* **2**, 114–118

Lugon M (2001). *Dealing with complaints.* British Association of Medical Managers, in press

Lugon M & Secker-Walker J (1999). Organisational framework for clinical governance. In Lugon M & Secker-Walker J (eds) *Cinical Governance. Making it Happen.* London: RSM Press, pp15–31

Lugon M & Secker-Walker J (2001). The organisation and clinical governance. In Lugon M & Secker-Walker J (eds) *Advancing Clinical Governance*. London: RMS Press

Miles A, Lugon M, Polychronis A (1996). The development of quality. I: Clinical practice. II: The derivation and implementation of clinical standards, guidelines and research evidence. In Miles A & Lugon M (eds) *Effective Clinical Practice*. Oxford: Blackwell Science, pp19–33

Secker-Walker J (1999). Clinical risk management. In: Lugon M & Secker-Walker J (eds) *Clinical Governance. Making it Happen*. London: RSM Press, pp 77–92

Sweeney K (2000). Patient experience. *Clinical Governance Bulletin* **1**, 6–7

Weight T, Phipps K, Jackson N (1999). Clinical governance and education and training. In Lugon M & Secker-Walker J (eds) *Clinical Governance. Making it Happen*. London: RSM Press, pp 131–142

Chapter 7

Clinical governance: a quality assurance audit system for regulating clinical practice

Bruce G Charlton

Introduction

Clinical governance is, at root, a very simple proposition. Clinical governance is reorganisation of the NHS such that it will embody an auditable 'quality assurance' system for the regulating and monitoring of clinical practice. In other words, clinical governance is a managerial system for controlling clinical activity.

Clinical governance as a 'quality assurance' system

The introduction of clinical governance has been marked by confusion over what kind of a thing it is. On the one hand, there appears very little substance behind the swirling declarations of high minded intentions (Goodman 1998), yet, at the same time, it is implausible that so much effort and so many resources would have been put into introducing clinical governance unless government and the NHS managerial hierarchy believed that they had something to gain.

We have been looking for clinical governance in the wrong place. Clinical governance is not a thing of substance, but a thing of style. It is not so much a pre-specified blueprint for change, as an aspiration. And that aspiration is that NHS managers (and via NHS managers, the government and their executive arm in the Department of Health) should substantially control clinical practice of the NHS.

And by 'clinical practice' is meant, for example, the specific details of what doctors do in the consultation – history taking, examination, investigation, treatment, prescription, referral and everything else that constitutes the activities of a doctor. For the first time, all this is to be brought under the control of the NHS general management hierarchy. This is the aspiration of clinical governance. This is what it means to say that the chief executive of a trust is to be 'responsible' for the quality clinical services: it means that the chief executive will control clinical practice. And there is a further expectation that control over clinical practice will be achieved by some version of 'quality assurance' (QA) auditing, where 'quality assurance' is defined in a technical managerial sense, as discussed below.

Clinical governance is not, therefore, an answer to the question of how to improve the 'quality' of clinical services. Nor is it a method for reducing malpractice or incompetence. Nor is it a means of ensuring that the NHS is of equal excellence throughout the United Kingdom, nor anything of this kind of thing. These may be hoped-for outcomes, or they may just be semi-plausible excuses for implementing the system, but the essence of clinical governance is that it is a system. Clinical governance intends that clinical medicine should be built around a quality assurance system. It is, of course, suggested when clinical practice is done according to a QA system, this will inevitably and continuously generate improvements in the quality and reliability of clinical practice. But there is not a shred of evidence to support this idea, so it is hard to take seriously. There is no historical or international precedent for running an excellent health service in this fashion. Indeed, the proposition that a quality assurance system applied to clinical medicine will improve medical practice is not explicitly asserted, nor argued, nor defended – it is just assumed.

The exact nature of a clinical governance QA system in the NHS is not predetermined. But the outline shape of the CG system is intended to be one based upon audit technologies (i.e., managerial methods derived from accountancy practice). Given past experience of public sector audit, it seems probable that CG will be dominated by audit of systems and processes, rather than audit of outcomes – this makes it an example of quality auditing (Feigenbaum 1983; Power 1997).

Corporate governance – the roots of clinical governance

The term 'clinical governance' is derived from *corporate* governance (Scally & Donaldson 1998). Corporate governance became talked about in 1992 following the Cadbury Report which was commissioned following several major contemporary financial scandals in which audit mechanisms had failed and the regulatory methods of corporations were judged to have been deficient (Cadbury Report 1992; Power 1997).

Although the Cadbury Report concluded that the main cause of vulnerability to financial mismanagement was inadequate auditing, it recommended that the best way of preventing such scandals was to have *more* auditing, but a new kind of auditing. The concept of corporate governance was launched, in which governance was 'the system by which companies are directed and controlled', and it was recommended that the focus of external auditing should be to ensure that an appropriate 'governance structure' was in place in an organisation (Nexia International 1996). External auditors should concentrate on 'assuring' that an adequate internal auditing system was up-and-running. Clinical governance is exactly this kind of 'governance structure', but applied to clinical activity instead of financial management.

This was a critical shift in auditing (Power 1997), away from traditional year-end auditing of outcomes designed to check that the books balanced, and towards ensuring that each organisation possessed an explicit 'governance structure' defining the flow of information within that organization, and auditing the processes which constitute that system. This was the shift from outcome to process that enabled the massive expansion of auditing which we see today in what has been termed the 'audit society' (Power 1997; Charlton, 1998). As Feigenbaum (1983) puts it: 'The quality-style audit assesses the effectiveness of implementation of the quality system and determines the degree to which systems objectives are being achieved. The audit is system – rather than product – oriented'.

Interestingly, the original thrust of the Cadbury Report was a concern with the 'transparency' and 'accountability' of senior executive managers and supervisory figures such as the Chairmen and non-executive directors of an organisation, and the opening up of senior managers to regulation. This was a response to the financial scandals of the early 1990s which stemmed mainly from corruption and incompetence among upper managerial staff. However, the concepts of transparency and accountability have been hijacked, and the apparatus captured by senior executives and turned against lower-level employees including professional practitioners. Senior managers never did become the subject, and instead became the controllers, of audit (Power 1997).

Quality assurance

Quality assurance (QA) does not have anything directly to do with assuring 'quality' in the real-world sense synonymous with 'excellence' – rather QA is a technical managerial term for auditing concentrated upon systems and processes rather than outcomes. Clinical governance adopts the Cadbury Report-derived idea that a properly constituted organisation should be based around a system of auditing systems and processes.

Quality assurance auditing has become closely identified with older managerial approaches including the word 'Quality' – such as Total Quality Management (TQM) and the awarding of quality assurance systems of organisations with British Standards and International Standards (Feigenbaum 1983; Perigord 1990; TQM International 1992). Quality assurance auditing therefore has close evolutionary links to 'quality enhancement' strategies, based upon creating a 'culture' centred on 'quality' which usually means reorganising production around reliable processes and systems of checking and feedback. These were in contrast to traditional assembly line 'quality control' inspections which focus upon testing the completed product and rejecting faulty items. These ideas are usually credited to the late W. Edward Deming, and also credited with generating the Japanese economic miracle of the post-1945 era. They enjoyed a belated revival among late twentieth century UK public sector organisations where they are still regarded as excitingly radical and promoted with messianic zeal.

When 'quality' has been redefined in terms of proper systems and processes, rather than proper outcomes, this has the effect of liberating 'quality enhancement' initiatives from the need to define desirable outcomes and best practice. This is of particular relevance to the NHS, since valid and reliable definitions of the real-world 'quality' (i.e., excellence) of clinical practices have proved impossible to agree upon in medicine. However, with the advent of QA, managers have no need to worry about whether they are measuring real-world quality. Debate has been shifted away from the contested territory of outcome measures, towards obtaining agreement to a standard system of practice – to make a fully explicit system of clinical QA in which all essential elements can be planned, documented and monitored. This has the effect of rendering clinical procedures at last amenable to external audit and hence external managerial control (Charlton 2000a).

Transparent and accountable

In other words, with the introduction of clinical governance as a QA system applied to clinical practice, proper clinical systems and procedures are conceptualised only as those which are transparent to auditing. To be 'transparent' to auditing is termed being 'accountable', and rendered a praiseworthy attribute (Charlton 1999b). Indeed, with the rise of the 'Audit Society' (Power 1997) to be 'opaque' to auditing is regarded as intrinsically suspicious, and 'unacceptable'. Yet, although transparency and accountability have become terms of approbation, strictly speaking they refer merely to audit-ability – and audit-ability does not legitimately carry any necessary implications of responsibility to the public, especially since auditing is implemented, performed and evaluated largely by managers and other bureaucrats.

The conflation of 'accountability with responsibility, and of 'transparency' with probity has arisen because, taking a lead from the Cadbury Report, modern managers equate a proper organisation with an auditable organisation. Organisations must be made auditable at any price. Traditional 'collegial' organisations of professionals, such as schools, universities, or hospitals, are regarded as intrinsically flawed, since managers do not know and cannot control what is going on in them. But, by its concentrations upon systems and procedures, QA provides a mechanism for quantifying almost any aspect of organisational performance that can be given a name – 'quality', 'equity', 'access' or whatever the current buzzword happens to be. Aspects of measured organisational performance that are attached to these terms can then 'objectively' be compared with pre-established criteria. What was unmeasurable has been rendered measurable, as if by magic, so long as one does not inquire too carefully into what words like 'quality' actually mean in operational terms.

So, QA auditing has profoundly re-shaped the perception of what constitutes a proper governance structure for an organisation. Proper practice has been redefined as auditable practice, and organisations (such as medical clinical practice in the NHS) whose procedures are insusceptible to audit are regarded as unacceptable. Such organisations are stigmatised as unaccountable – implying irresponsible – and lacking in transparency – implying deliberately secretive. The present climate of uncritical advocacy misses the obvious point that audit of processes is merely a crude managerial technique, and far from being a panacea, QA has a very poor track record within the UK public sector.

Why anyone should imagine that QA methods are suitable for controlling all forms of human activity is an interesting question. Yet this wildly improbable belief is the norm among UK public sector managers, and forms the basis for implementing clinical governance. Apparently, the UK government and their civil servants and administrators are in the grip of some form of mass psychopathology. However, there is more to it than that.

The meaning of 'quality' – the example of university teaching

Since, under QA, organisations are no longer seen in terms of outcomes, but in terms of systems and procedures, it follows that proper organisational structure is seen to be fully systematised, fully documented, fully auditable, hence fully controllable by those who can set the agenda for auditing. And a QA system has no obvious limit to its range. Criteria for measuring quality, excellence, equity, or any other desired attribute, can usually be defined in terms of 'proper' systems and procedures on the basis of no more than superficial face-plausibility. It comes down to a question of names.

For example, criteria to measure the real-world quality of university teaching proved impossible to agree upon. Instead, the 'quality' of teaching was re-defined by the QAA (Quality Assurance Agency for Higher Education) in terms of compliance with the quality assurance system (Charlton 1999b, 2000a). Teaching characterised by flow-charts, planning, documentation and internal audit was defined as 'high quality'. Only that which is 'on paper', hence auditable, is deemed to count as legitimate teaching activity. No attempt was made to prove that this method of organising and evaluating teaching inevitably lead to 'high quality', nor that this method of teaching-by-numbers was superior to previously practised methods of teaching. The QA-approved system was high quality by definition.

All existing evidence is that QA-driven teaching is vastly inferior to traditional methods: there has never been a university of acknowledged excellence in teaching run in this fashion. Excellent universities in the world and throughout history have taught in many many different ways but never in a fashion which would meet with QAA approval. Indeed, because of its high transaction costs, teachers spend more time on documentation and less on teaching. QA also causes a shift in resources away from teaching and towards auditing, and a shift in power away from academics and towards managers, auditors and the politicians who set the audit agenda. And since managers, auditors and the politicians are more remote and more difficult to influence than academics, there is also a reduction in the power of students. What goes on in universities – from admission, to what is taught, how it is taught, how it is examined and the degrees awarded – are all coming increasingly under centralised control.

Debate on the subject of quality of university teaching was swamped by the QAA-generated mass of pseudo-objective cross-referenced explicit documentation concerning 'standards' and 'performance'. All competent authorities agreed that there has been a decline in the real-world quality of university teaching (with many more students and much less in the way of teachers and teaching resources, this decline is a near-certainty as a general observation). But QAA inspections do not measure real-world teaching quality – indeed they make no attempt to measure real-world quality. Instead 'teaching quality' is re-defined as that which is measured by the QAA audit.

Quality assurance as a managerial technology

Freeman Dyson (1997) described how societal change can be driven by ideas, but more often it is driven by technologies with the ideas left trying to keep-up. Quality assurance auditing can be seen as a technology for management.

Physics has been driven by ideas such as those of Newton and Einstein, but also by technologies such as the telescope and the particle accelerator. Technologies enhance the situation of some social groups and damage the position of others: breakthroughs in spinning and weaving cloth during the eighteenth century destroyed the livelihoods of independent male craftsmen and led to the growth of mill factories employing women and children – the factory owners became rich and powerful, the displaced weavers starved to death (Bronowski 1943).

Technologies are adopted because they serve the interests of social groups with power. The telescope made Galileio a rich man because he could provide a service for the dominant merchant class (Bronowski 1973). Control of a large particle accelerator makes a scientist powerful and prestigious (Taubes 1986). Only to the extent that career enhancement coincides with good science does new technology enhance science (Hull 1988). Much the same applies to medicine. In the past, technologies were adopted that served the interests of the power groups of the time: doctors, patient groups, industrial corporations and mass public opinion (Le Fanu 1999). Nowadays, medical technologies more closely support the interests of the ascendant class of managers.

Quality assurance usually describes itself as an ideology, a set of aspirations harnessed to a transforming ethos. For example, it is often said that a QA system is one which puts 'quality' at the centre of an organisation, or an ideology which subordinates an organisation to 'the needs of the customer'. So QA is presented as a new ideology of management. But the implementation of QA systems very seldom attains the ideal of a quality-centred ethos permeating corporate life. In practice, QA is almost always something that managers do to employees. In practice, QA systems in schools, in universities, in local government and in the police have been imposed upon the practitioners that actually do the work by a new class of managerial regulators. Indeed, the ideology of clinical governance is a very old one – essentially the ideal of 'rational' and 'efficient' administration that has driven many previous bureaucratic expansions as diverse as Bismarck's Germany, Taylorian 'scientific' management' in the USA, 'economic planning' in Britain, and the Command Economies of the USSR and Eastern bloc, China and India. So the ideals of QA are certainly not novel.

What is novel is the technology of QA auditing. This really is a new technology – a new tool for the management of organisations. And, like other technologies, its use has spread primarily because it serves the interests of those with power.

What is new about QA is the technology of auditing applied to systems and processes. And it has spread because it is more effective from a managerial perspective than the previous system of managing organisations. In other words, QA has spread because it is good for managers.

Clinical governance and quality assurance auditing

What will clinical governance be like assuming that it is implemented in something like the form its advocates envisage? This is not a difficult question to answer, because general models of the effects of QA auditing systems are readily available from other organisations in the UK public sector already – in local government functions, the police, schools and further- and higher-education. For instance, OFSTED (Office For Standards in Education) is the enforcement arm of QA in schools, auditing teaching against nationally-defined standard practices. The QAA does a similar job in universities.

It is known that OFSTED and QAA are both extremely bureaucratic, generate massive paperwork, and inflict heavy opportunity costs on auditees (Charlton 2000b). OFSTED is also notorious as a cause of psychopathology among teachers due to overwork, uncertainty, and fear of victimisation in the event of failure. OFSTED inspections seem to be a significant factor leading to teachers retiring early and leaving the profession. Doctors can expect the same kind of pressure from a clinical governance system.

The QAA inspection of my own medium-sized university department (approximately 15 academic staff) generated considerably more than ten thousand pieces of paper housed in dozens of box-files that filled a room, and the inspection lasted four full days. The logistics of preparation took many months including full- and part-time secondment of several academic and secretarial staff, dozens of hours of meetings and 'away days' involving dozens of staff, and temporary employment of extra secretarial help.

While the QAA central bureaucracy is itself a relatively small organisation, and relatively inexpensive for the government, the heavy cost of inspection is borne by the department being audited. Nationally, it has been estimated that the QAA Subject Review exercise has probably cost several hundred million pounds in opportunity costs. Similarly, the costs of clinical governance bureaucracy cannot be estimated from the central bureaucracy – the indirect costs to the clinical organisations operating under the system would account for the bulk of costs.

The nature of auditing: cross-checking for consistency

The bureaucratic and invasive nature of QA auditing derives from financial auditing, and the principal purpose of financial auditing is to detect and deter incompetence and dishonesty in the handling of money. Incompetence is relatively straightforward to discover – but it is the claim of audit to detect dishonest dealing which requires further examination (Charlton 2000b).

There is an apparent paradox involved in auditing. At first sight, it might seem that checking the books fails to solve the problem of dishonesty. After all, if a practitioner is not trusted to do their job honestly, then why should they keep the books honestly?

The answer is that audit detects fraud through cross-checking for inconsistencies. It could be said that the essence of audit is the search for discrepancies in documentation (Perigord 1990). Fraud is detected when 'the books don't balance'. Cross-checking works when the accounts contain independent sources of evidence, making-up a web of money flows that constitute the operations of the organisation. Each strand of the web should be consistent with each other strand when checked every-which-way. A large organisation has so many strands that the number of potential cross-checks is almost infinite. Anyone wishing to 'cook the books' has a great deal to fake if they are to ensure that every possible inconsistency has been ironed out.

Fraud is therefore apparent to an auditor, especially when the volume and inter-connectedness of organizational activity is unmanageably large, and when it involves many people. In effect, the auditor is like a detective who takes a statement from each witness to a crime, then checks that each witness' 'story' is consistent with all of the others. For example, in his 'how to do it' manual of quality auditing, Mills (1993) describes the ways in which an auditor can use cross-questioning and observation to catch the auditee in various types of discrepancy. It is a basic assumption that inconsistency is evidence either of incompetence or dishonesty. Discrepancies are assumed to constitute attempts to cover-up fraud.

Financial accounting (usually) works in its job of deterring and detecting fraud because it is (usually) easier, cheaper and more efficient to be honest than it is to prepare internally-consistent fake accounts which can stand up to skilled cross-checking. In other words, true accounts automatically balance when cross-checked because they are a reflection of reality, while it takes a great deal of work to create audit-proof false accounts.

Clinical governance – checking for medical incompetence and dishonesty against guideline-based norms

QA auditing has many analogies with financial auditing. But instead of monitoring cash flows to detect financial fraud, a quality assurance system monitors compliance to a quality assurance system – it monitors that such a system is in place, and is functioning. But instead of money, the currency is information.

Clinical governance will audit doctors on their compliance to particular, guideline-based, norms of clinical practice. The specific content of guidelines does not much matter – what is vital is that there are guidelines, and that they are complied with. The approved CG system is one in which, ultimately, it is intended that every significant aspect of practice is formally and explicitly planned, documented and monitored. What is not documented does not count as significant, because it cannot be part of the QA system, hence cannot be audited. Good clinical practice is defined by clinical governance in terms of an explicit information flow system: whatever is implicit, or outside of the system, does not count as good practice.

Making medicine auditable is therefore what guideline-based practice is all about, at least from a managerial perspective. This explains the vast amount of manpower and resources which NHS management has invested in guidelines over the past few years – creating and funding an army of researchers (health economists, epidemiologists, biostatisticians, health service researchers, facilitators and administrators) in the process. Ultimately, clinical governance guidelines will be expressed in terms of flow diagrams ('care pathways') as in managed healthcare systems or the treatment plans used in some Health Maintenance Organisations in the USA. The flow diagrams are necessary to QA auditing because they define the relationship of information sources, and the legitimate range of cross-checking between information flows. Armed with these diagrams of what is supposed to happen, the clinical governance enforcers will behave very much like financial auditors in their search for inconsistencies. And inconsistency implies fraud – and in medicine fraud translates as malpractice.

A CG system would audit clinical practice documentation for its completeness (minimum data set) and each item of documentation must be consistent with all other items of documentation when cross-checked. Undocumented practice is bad practice and the nature and level of documentation will be defined by managerial demands, not by clinical need. Practice must also be consistent with the mission statements, and aims and objectives, of the organisation, and documentation must be provided to demonstrate this consistency.

And as the CG system becomes more comprehensive, so the potential for cross-checking will increase. Each specific item of information must also be consistent with the documentation from other professionals in the organisation, and with other disciplines. Internal information can be checked for its consistency with external policies, such as relevant government or NHS executive policies (such as Patients Charter, waiting list initiatives, ethnic monitoring or whatever is the latest high profile project). All this cross-checking inevitably requires vast documentation, hence vast bureaucracy, hence substantial cost (Charlton 2000b). And this is the essential reason why QA systems have an irresistible tendency to become highly bureaucratic and expensive. Escalation of documentation is built-in, even when this is not the initial intention and when the early phases are relatively modest and sensible.

The fact that auditors could not conceivably read all the vast documentation, let alone perform the almost infinite number of potential cross-checks, does not matter. The point is that the auditors might want to know anything. And failure of either comprehensiveness of documentation or consistency in cross-checking in any one respect is taken as evidence of generalised failure. If the auditee has failed to stick to recommended procedure (failure to 'stick to guidelines'), then the auditee is culpable.

In the end, for QA auditing to prevent 'fraud', it is driven into making the demands for documentation so comprehensive that fakery is easily established by cross checking, and so heavily labour intensive and multidisciplinary that fake accounting will not be an option. It must be made easier to comply with the letter of the audit than it is to cook the books. So, in practice, QA systems will always generate a demand for vast quantities of documentation, whatever the hopes or promises of its advocates.

Trust in process, distrust of people

Audit systems such as CG displace trust onto the process of audit rather than the individual employee (Power 1997). Instead of trusting employees to do their job properly, employees are made to comply with audit procedures and trusted only to prepare auditable documentation. The practitioner is not trusted to perform well, but the audit process is trusted to ensure good performance.

Audit systems such as clinical governance therefore mark a stark reversal of assumptions for the medical profession. In the past, doctors have been trusted except where there was reason to assume that trust was being abused. Doctors were assumed to be doing their job unless it could be shown otherwise. But under clinical governance these principles are inverted. Audit is based upon an assumption that doctors are incompetent frauds, except when documentation can prove that they are not. The assumption is that doctors are not doing their job properly, except where documentation demonstrates that they are. Failure to comply with procedure is sufficient evidence of incompetence or fraud.

For example, re-accreditation or re-validation are being absorbed into the clinical governance structure. In the past a medical qualification was a license to practise, and removal of that license required that the practitioner be proved unfit to practise. Now the principle is reversed and the medical qualification means very little. Practice is conditional upon compliance with re-validation or re-accreditation procedures, which are already being driven by managerial and political imperatives. The future seems clear enough. If a doctor does not jump through managerial hoops in a manner which satisfies managers then he or she will not be allowed to practise. The primary medical virtue will become obedience not competence.

Managerial control by QA auditing

Corporate governance put forward the idea that legitimate corporate functioning depends upon audit, that audit is primarily a matter of regulatory systems and that the role of the auditor is to ensure that the appropriate governance structures are in place and operating properly.

Traditional outcomes auditing is retrospective and seeks to impose good practice only by its deterrent effect. If you commit fraud, the books will not balance, and the auditors will catch you. By contrast QA auditing is – in intention, if not always in practice – prospective. The name tells us that QA seeks to assure good practice, not to detect bad practice. Quality is operationalised by defining good practice as adherence to a specific set of systems and processes. In medicine, this translates into good clinical practice which is defined as clinical practice based upon documented adherence to pre-planned guidelines, protocols, standards etc. As described above, the 'high quality' good doctor is defined by obedience to the QA system of conditional re-accreditation and continued documented compliance with guideline-based practice.

Politicians, managers or anyone else can come to control a 'quality assured' organisation by 'capturing' its audit system. Inspections and audit cycles are linked to incentives (such as differential funding, published league tables, withdrawal of funding, threat of closure, imposition of external management, scapegoating or naming-and-shaming). An organisation that wishes to do well in a QA inspection will need to provide evidence that there are procedures in place of the recommended kind, and that these procedures are operating. Documented compliance with procedure is taken to mean that the organization can 'assure' whatever is required by the controllers.

For example, if governments want to encourage an NHS trust to work more closely with local authorities, it can do this by QA mechanisms. Government might set-up an external agency (OFLOC?) whose job is to audit NHS Trusts and relevant branches of Local Authority for compliance with a system of standard procedures that are assumed to represent cooperation (e.g., monthly joint policy meetings, joint appointment of liaison managers, two-way circulation of newsletters etc.). NHS trusts and local authorities might then be inspected by OFLOC to ensure these systems and procedures are in place and functioning. An NHS trust that wants to do well in the audit will need to set up formal structures for policy, liaison, feedback and so on - and provide documentation that these structures are operating. If the trust 'failed' an OFLOC inspection by providing insufficient or inconsistent documentation it could experience a funding penalty with job losses and hostile media coverage.

Yet only insofar as it can reasonably be assumed the demands of auditors – and the politicians and managers who devise the standards which auditors enforce – are identical with excellence, can QA be said to be genuinely about enhancing quality.

Advantages of audit-based management

In old fashioned 'command' systems of management, the managers must directly 'order' the workers to perform certain tasks. This raises the problem of enforcing obedience. Orders will either need to be face-to-face, via an intermediary (e.g., a foreman), or by written instructions 'memo'). However it is done, this style of command management involves an element of direct confrontation, of one person asserting their will over another person, and achieving dominance.

When managers are more skilled, better educated, of higher status and more confident than the workers, attaining dominance is not usually a problem. Indeed, imposing dominance on others, bending them to your will, is enjoyable for some people. But when, as in the NHS, the workers include people such as doctors who are more skilled, better educated, higher status and more confident than the managers who were supposed to command them – this makes command style management difficult and unpleasant at best, and impossible at worst (Charlton 2000b).

As audit technologies have evolved away from outcomes and towards systems and processes, difficult policy decisions and unpleasant personal confrontations have been exported outside the organisation executive, away from the corporate management and onto third-party groups. Managerial consultants are used to generate standards, guidelines and protocols, and in the public sector, enforcement has been devolved to external agency auditors such as OFSTED and QAA. For example, in the NHS, it is envisaged the NICE will generate guidelines, and CHIMP will enforce them. Both NICE and CHIMP are third parties detached from executive control, but both are NHS managerial appointees and employees, ensuring that their actions will not be independent of the demands of politicians and NHS executives. By many such manoeuvers, NHS managers have retained power but shifted responsibility, have retained control but shifted the locus of dissent and resistance onto third parties.

At least in the UK, QA therefore appears to be an evolution of managerial technology, a style of management which, from the managers' perspective, is superior to previous styles of management such as a direct command system. QA is superior not in the sense of improving the performance of the organisation, but in the sense that QA works more effectively to promote the interests of managers. In particular, it enables managers of low-level expertise and modest individual dominance, to impose their will upon expert and personally forceful people – a description that would fit many doctors.

The 'success' of QA auditing

There is no doubt that quality assurance is a success story. The big question concerns the nature of this success.

The managerial technology of auditing, especially of systems and processes, has swept the UK, especially the public sector. Accountancy firms have expanded enormously and come to dominate the vast and highly paid workforce of 'management consultants', which in their turn attract many of the most highly motivated and best educated of the workforce. This has so affected the organisation of large corporations that our contemporary world has been characterised as 'The Audit Society' (Power 1997).

Professionals seem powerless to resist. The idea that QA auditing is able to assure quality seems to have been accepted without even asking for proof. There has been no debate over the principles of CG, just moaning about the details of implementation. It has not been noticed that doctors are being stripped of professional autonomy and reduced to the role of functionaries. So far, clinical governance has been a major success story for government and managers.

Yet when the specific individual areas in which quality assurance has been introduced are subjected to appraisal, it appears very obvious that the performance of core functions of organisations is usually severely damaged by these managerial systems. Of course there are almost certain to be some benefits when vast and expensive re-organisations are imposed. Nonetheless, it is clear that the real success story of QA is that it is extremely beneficial to the power, rewards and career prospects of managers.

Typically these gains in the career trajectory of managers are attained at the expense of practitioners. There is a power shift away from 'doing' and towards 'regulating' (Power 1997; Charlton 1998). Although managers put themselves forward as advocates of the consumer interest, and a QA-dominated organisation typically makes use of customer surveys, focus groups, feedback from users etc., this evidence is collected at the behest of managers, and it is managers who are responsible for selection, analysis and interpretation of this information.

So, although QA has not been successful in improving services, it has been extremely successful in promoting the career trajectory of managers. That seems to be the key factor behind the widespread adoption of QA.

Quality assurance auditing has spread through the public sector and has now reached the NHS in the guise of clinical governance. Clinical governance is fundamentally parasitic, a system of regulation that will enhance the power and prospects of the managerial class at the expense of the clinical practitioners who actually do the work of the NHS. And, like most parasites, clinical governance will tend to weaken, and may eventually kill, its host.

The fact that this lethal remedy is being applied with the excuse of 'improving quality' is merely one of the more ironic aspects of this tawdry tale.

References

Bronowski J (1943). *William Blake, 1757–1827: A Man Without a Mask.* London: Secker & Warburg

Bronowski J (1973). *The Ascent of Man.* London: BBC

Cadbury Report (1992). *Report of the Committee on The Financial Aspects of Corporate Governance.* London: Gee and Co. Ltd.

Charlton BG (1998). Essay review of *The Audit Society* by Michael Power. *Journal of Evaluation in Clinical Practice* **4**, 249–53
Charlton BG (1999a). The ideology of 'accountability'. *Journal of the Royal College of Physicians of London* **33**, 33–5
Charlton BG (1999b). QAA: why we should not collaborate. *Oxford Magazine* **169**, 8–10
Charlton BG (2000a). The new management of scientific knowledge: a change of direction with profound implications. In: Miles A, Hampton JR, Hurwitz B (eds), *NICE, CHI and the NHS reforms: Enabling Excellence or Imposing Control?* London: Aesculapius Medical Press
Charlton BG (2000b). QAA: 'light touch' auditing is not an option. *Oxford Magazine* **176**, 12–13
Feigenbaum AV (1983). *Total Quality Control: Third edition*. New York, NY: McGraw Hill
Freeman Dyson J (1997). *Imagined Worlds*. Cambridge, MA: Harvard University Press
Goodman NW (1998). Clinical governance. *British Medical Journal* **317**, 1725–7
Hull DL (1988). *Science as a Process*. Chicago, IL: Chicago University Press
Le Fanu J (1999). *The Rise and Fall of Western Medicine*. London: Little, Brown and Co
Mills D (1993). *Quality Auditing*. London: Chapman and Hall
Nexia International (1996). *International Handbook of Corporate Governance*. London: International Thomson Business Press
Perigord M (1990). *Achieving Total Quality Management*. Cambridge, MA: Productivity Press
Power M (1997). The Audit Society; Rituals of Verification. Oxford: Oxford University Press
TQM International (1992). *BS 5750/ IOS 9000 Handbook*. Frodsham: TQM International
Scally G & Donaldson LJ (1998). Clinical governance and the drive for quality improvement in the new NHS in England. *British Medical Journal* **317**, 61–5
Taubes Gary (1986). *Nobel Dreams: Power, Deceit and the Ultimate Experiment*. Redmond, WA: Tempus Press

Chapter 8

Clinical governance: a political answer to a complex and insoluble problem

Neville W Goodman

Introduction

The term 'clinical governance' is credited to Professor Liam Donaldson, and appeared in a government White Paper in 1997 (Department of Health 1997). Shortly before he was made Chief Medical Officer in 1998, an explanation of clinical governance co-written by Donaldson was published (Scally *et al.* 1998), which was probably the first explanation seen widely by doctors in the UK. The same journal published my criticisms of clinical governance (Goodman 1998), which were that the description was vague and lacking in detail, that the authors clearly understood the real difficulties – how to improve leadership, and how to define quality – but gave no clue of how to solve them, that reliance on rhetoric is counterproductive when aimed at people who have seen similar tactics used before and that it is not enough to make an untried system a statutory duty. At the time, I thought it unlikely that clinical governance would deliver an improvement in the quality of healthcare.

The lack of intellectual debate about how clinical governance will work has been disappointing. The good things are constantly repeated, but criticisms are ignored. Over the winter of 1999–2000, many of us in the acute sector of the NHS saw the serious effects of bed and staff shortages. Clinical governance, especially with the lack (until the budget of March 2000) of central financial support exacerbating the shortages, did not improve matters and has turned out to be yet another distracting reorganisation.

There are no simple answers to the problems of something as complicated as the NHS. Whether intended or not, the politicians give the impression that they understand the problems better than the people working within the service. The inevitable result is disillusion. The most important elements in the delivery of quality in healthcare are contained in the relations between human beings. With good working relationships, clinical governance (or whatever it's called) happens naturally.

In this chapter, I am not concerned with whether clinical governance has worked or can work: to a large extent that depends on how clinical governance is interpreted locally. I am concerned with how clinical governance was presented, and how it has continued to be presented, despite criticism. With the editors' and publishers' permission, I have drawn heavily on two of my own already published articles: 'Clinical governance', which appeared in the *British Medical Journal* (Goodman 1998) and 'Accountability, clinical governance and the acceptance of imperfection', which appeared in the *Journal of the Royal Society of Medicine* (Goodman 2000a).

Setting the scene

Scally and Donaldson's article appeared in a thematic issue of the *British Medical Journal* celebrating and examining the first 50 years of the NHS and thinking about its future. The article was titled 'Clinical governance and the drive for quality improvement in the new NHS in England' (Scally & Donaldson 1998). Doctors of my acquaintance fell into one of three groups in their response. Some, like me, started out cynical and remain deeply cynical about something seen as little more than a political exercise to divert attention from the real deficiencies in the NHS. Some of them have spoken out, but most sigh deeply and get on with their clinical work. Others have not thought about it at all, dismissing it as irrelevant. But some have embraced it (although, as I will show, at the time there was nothing of substance to embrace). The obvious justification for clinical governance is that quality is important, and anything that will improve quality must be embraced. My answer to this is simple: first show me that it will improve quality. (The conflation of quality and excellence with the means supposed to provide them is dealt with by Loughlin, Chapter 1.)

Another common justification for embracing clinical governance is as a tool to enable us to get more resources. Within a limited health budget – and the budget will remain limited however much more we are to have – clinical governance will only enable hospitals that are better at it to get resources shifted towards them; but we were not *given* the tool at all. We were shown the tool in the shop window, we were told what it does, although without any test results, but we were not told how to use it or how it works. For all sorts of reasons, including an over-reliance on the more hardline sort of evidence-based medicine (Goodman 2000b) and difficulties measuring the quality of vastly differing sorts of healthcare (Parry *et al.* 1998; Rothwell *et al.* 1999; Signorini *et al.* 1999; Frankel *et al.* 2000; Stark *et al.* 2000), the tool is unreliable and blunt, and with a tendency to slip. What's more, clinical governance was first introduced as yet another cost-neutral addition to the work done by NHS staff.

What if the White Paper of 1997, instead of introducing clinical governance, had started with the admission that we get healthcare on the cheap in Britain? As with clinical governance itself, this is speculation rather than hypothesis because it is not testable. (How *will* we know if clinical governance has worked? The cynical answer is that it will have worked if the government, and more pertinently the media, decide it has worked.) Even if no more money had been put into the NHS then, how much money would by now have been saved by *not* having to have set up clinical governance committees and the means to service them? Clinical governance was yet another reorganisation: 'The political remedy for the chronic underfunding of the NHS has been perpetual revolution through reorganisation … exploiting the apparently bottomless pit of clinical productivity.' (Pollock & Dunnigan 2000).

Deconstruction

I described clinical governance (as explained by Scally & Donaldson) as the next 'Big Idea' intended to solve all the problems of the NHS (Goodman 1998). My original title was dropped in the editing; with allusion to Hans Christian Andersen's emperor, it was 'Deconstructing Clinical Governance: Scally and Donaldson's new clothes'.

Articles in medical journals have substance (the data or findings) and they have style (the way those data or findings are described). Scally and Donaldson's article did not have substance in the same sense as a standard medical article, because there were no data or findings. This is true for any article whose main theme is ethical or philosophical: the way the article is written becomes the substance of the article. It is then a matter of distinguishing between the two meanings of the word rhetoric, which are 'the art of effective or persuasive speaking or writing' and 'language designed to persuade or impress' (see also Loughlin, Chapter 1). (I fully realise that in teasing these out of Scally and Donaldson's article, I lay myself open to the same analysis, and that also the boundary between labelling writing as effective and persuasive, and as *designed* to persuade or impress is partly subjective.)

Scally and Donaldson's article started well, with a clear statement that we need to get away from the obsession with money introduced by the previous, Conservative, administration. They wrote that 'A commitment to deliver high quality care should be at the heart of everyday clinical practice', with which no reasonable person could disagree (and which is therefore covered by Charlton's definition of a platitude, Chapter 7). They continued, 'In the past many health professionals have watched as board agendas and management meetings have become dominated by financial issues and activity targets', which was recognition of something that had worried clinicians from the time of the Conservatives' 1989 White Paper. Their introduction ended, 'The government's white paper on the NHS in England outlines a new style of NHS that will redress this imbalance.'

What was now needed, but was lacking, was a clear, concrete description of how clinical governance would do this. There had been a clue to this lack in the rhetoric of the title of the article: 'Clinical governance and the drive for quality improvement in the *new* NHS in England' (my italics). This appellation – the *new* NHS – came directly from Labour's White paper. *New* Labour wants everything to be new: new is better. But there's no natural law that says this is true, and an obsession with new is an insult to the elderly, who cannot be new no matter how they try. It could even be argued that Labour – by turning away from domination by financial issues and activity targets – was returning the NHS more to how it was before the Conservatives damaged it.

I read 'Clinical governance and the drive for quality improvement in the new NHS in England' (Scally & Donaldson 1998) very carefully, word by word, and some parts more than once. I really tried hard to understand why it needed over four pages of the *British Medical Journal* to impart the common sense message that we must all strive after quality in practising medicine. The essay was all thought and no action, an epitome of hope over expectation, a high-sounding clarion call of wonderful things just over the horizon. Most depressing of all, the authors clearly recognised the real difficulties – including the problem of working in teams with poor leadership, the difficulties of finding valid ways to measure quality in specialties that do not have the hard outcomes of surgery, and the difficulties of getting the conclusions of medical audit into practice – but they ignored just how obdurate these difficulties are. The result was an essay full of the 'what', but short on the 'how'.

It was also extremely wordy in laying out the 'what'. To describe clinical governance as 'rigorous in its application, organisation-wide in its emphasis, developmental in its thrust, and positive in its connotations' is writing to impress, not to enlighten. They could just as easily have written 'rigorous in its thrust, positive in its emphasis, developmental in its application, and organisation-wide in its connotations', or any other combination. By way of developing this idea, they went on to write that 'Although clinical governance can be viewed generally as positive and developmental, it will also be seen as a way of addressing concerns about the quality of healthcare.'

The opening clause of this sentence starts with 'Although', which suggests that the following clause will be in logical contrast, i.e., the sentence could be rephrased 'Clinical governance can be viewed generally as positive and developmental, but it will also be seen as a way of addressing concerns about the quality of healthcare.' But surely 'addressing concerns about ... quality' *is* positive. Surely, concern about quality is the *whole point* of clinical governance?

Unlike many of the other proposed changes to the NHS over the last few years, such as achieving a balance, or continuing medical education, clinical governance as a phrase was meaningless to medical professionals. We were depending on others to explain it to us, so we needed to be clear what they meant. They wrote that clinical governance is a way of 'addressing' concerns, but we want our concerns *allayed*. The verb address was used eight more times in the article, meaning variously 'cover' (a range of performances), 'solve' (as in problem solving), 'deal with' (poor performance), 'enable' (good performance), and 'correct' (a weakness).

This is poor use of language, which, sadly, was a pointer to poor use of language throughout the article. I agree entirely that 'Medical directors of NHS trusts may recognise that they have skill deficits, but although these may be addressed when someone is in post, a proactive approach would undoubtedly be preferable', but I would have expressed it as 'It is better for medical directors of NHS trusts to make sure they have all the necessary skills before they take up their posts'.

Coming up to their conclusion they wrote that, 'A renewed commitment to the accuracy, appropriateness, completeness, and analysis of healthcare information will be required if judgements about clinical quality are to be made and the impact of clinical governance is to be assessed. These issues are so important and have been so unsatisfactorily dealt with in the past that they will need to be addressed (which means tackled) nationally ...'

It was all very well writing of a renewed *commitment*, but how could we collect all this information accurately and assess it properly (even supposing we knew how to do it) with no committed resources? And what is the evidence that these things 'have been so unsatisfactorily dealt with in the past'? I cannot know, but the political context of clinical governance leads me to believe this was an allusion to some well publicised medical incidents (the excess deaths after paediatric cardiac surgery in Bristol, the failure of the Kent and Canterbury cervical screening service, the GMC's striking-off the gynaecologist Ledward for shocking malpractice and the Shipman case etc.). There will always be bad practice, but these examples – without any comparators, in other countries for example – are not evidence of the complete failure of the system.

There is no doubt that these medical incidents were an important stimulus to the development of clinical governance. Despite reassurances that poor performance is only one aspect of clinical governance, people in command such as the Prime Minister, Secretaries of State and health Ministers, the Chief Medical Officer, and other subordinates, do seem to concentrate unduly upon it. One obvious reason is that it sometimes seems to be the *only* aspect that interests the media.

An illustrative example

New ideas are often best explained by example. Scally and Donaldson (1998) presented an imagined interview for the post of medical director of a failing trust – the 'Gridstone Royal Infirmary NHS Trust'. The appointment panel ask non-specific questions about the applicant's 'vision' of clinical governance, and the applicant answers with generalities: 'mechanisms for effective clinical audit', 'learn from complaints', 'clear skills and competencies'. If I had been on the panel I would have asked, 'How?' Eventually a panel member does ask, 'Okay, could you be a bit more specific?'

But our imaginary applicant offers nothing but more empty phrases, more about wrong culture, minimum of hierarchies, environments of learning and evaluation, leadership skills of staff nurses, and so on. She says that patients must be more involved but, to take one example of consumer choice in the United States, mothers-to-be tend to choose between obstetric services because of free diapers or baby buggies, rather than on the standard of medical care.

How would clinical governance be done?

According to what was described as a 'useful framework document' that came from a local British Medical Association group, developing clinical governance needed the setting-up of a committee, meeting monthly. This committee was to:

1. Implement recommendations from the National Institute for Clinical Excellence and the National Service Framework.
2. Review recommendations from DEC reports, Cochrane Reviews, evidence-based mental health, and other bodies, and ensure appropriate action occurs.
3. Recommend the use of care plans where appropriate.
4. Implement the use of clinical guidelines where appropriate.
5. Keep policies and guidelines under review and ensure appropriate implementation and audit is occurring.
6. Ensure any service developments meet quality standards, including implementation of new drugs and therapeutics.
7. Consider research proposals.
8. Consider standards from professional practice groups within the trust.
9. Prepare quality clinical practice reports for the clinical governance steering group – another monthly committee but with limited membership.

Even allowing that this committee would incorporate some already existing committees, its work is impossibly wide-ranging, and not something fitting easily with a large clinical commitment. The list is a product of unthinking acceptance of the idea of clinical governance: why should we put our trust in the recommendations of these bodies (Goodman 2000b) to the extent that all clinicians (which includes nurses, and paramedical staff as well as doctors) be required by this committee to follow them? And who will have what sanctions over staff who do not follow them?

Integration or disintegration

Drawing all their threads together, Scally & Donaldson (1998) presented a hexagon with the legend 'Integrating approaches of Clinical Governance'. Each segment represented a feature of clinical governance and each had a number of listed items:

1. Coherence: goals of individual, team, and organisation aligned; excellent ommunications; external partnerships forged.
2. Risk avoidance: well-trained staff; clear procedures; safe environment.
3. Poor performance: early recognition; decisive intervention; effective self-regulation; feedback on performance.
4. Infrastructure: access to evidence; time allowed to plan; training and development strategies; information technology supports practice.

5. Culture: open and participative; good leadership; education and research valued; patient partnership; ethos of teamwork.
6. Quality methods: good practice spread; clinical policies evidence based; lessons learned from failure; improvement processes integrated.

This is a wish-list: it is the 'high-sounding clarion call of wonderful things just over the horizon' that I referred to earlier. These are the features of a health service working perfectly. When you had them all, you could call it clinical governance. It does not work the other way round: you cannot impose clinical governance on health workers and get this system. Life, and people, do not behave in that way. To take a small example from personal experience: 'goals of individual, team, and organisation aligned' appears against the feature 'coherence', which provokes a wry smile from anyone, like me, who has sat on a hospital car park management group. More seriously, there is again the concern about 'evidence': what of the large areas of healthcare practice for which there is no evidence?

I put a similar hexagon in my article, which I titled 'Disintegration of Clinical Governance':

1. Politics: vested interests; spin doctors; rhetoric; hidden agendas.
2. Bureaucracy: perpetual reorganisations; computer incompatibilities; paperwork.
3. Expectations: doctors; managers; patients and relatives; pressure groups.
4. Culture: perceptions; societal values; ethics.
5. Resources: time constraints; too few beds; unfilled posts; lack of money.
6. Incoherence: lack of evidence; conflicting guidelines; exhaustion.

This list gives me no satisfaction, but it is reality. The 'winter pressures' of 1999–2000 moved us firmly to the segment labelled 'resources', and thence to incoherence due to exhaustion.

Criticisms of clinical governance

My criticisms of clinical governance themselves attracted criticism, although disappointingly not from Scally and Donaldson. Kieran Walshe accused me (Walshe 2000) of denying all attempts to measure quality, just because it is sometimes difficult. But there *are* aspects of quality in healthcare that *can* be measured, and from which we can improve medical care. He disagreed with my less aggressive attitude to the measurement of quality, which I summarised by suggesting that the key was 'good working relations' within the service. He criticised me for using this phrase, adding 'whatever that means'. It is indeed an empty phrase, one of those difficult-to-define-things that leads people to say, 'I can't exactly say what it is, but I know it when I see it.' But the irony is that Scally and Donaldson's article, which

Walshe was defending, was full of these phrases – especially in their example of the failing Gridstone Royal Infirmary NHS Trust.

Walshe disagreed with me that the effect of clinical guidelines would be, as I put it, 'hordes of people ticking boxes on other people's work'. But when a Medical Protection Society newsletter describes the test of successful clinical governance as 'when a chief executive can ask about evidence-based practice in any given specialty and be given a response that conforms to best practice guidelines and protocols', it is hard not to remain uneasy. As chief executives will not come and ask individual practitioners, this will have to be done by some process similar to ticking boxes. And this test of 'successful' clinical governance begs the question (see above) what makes guidelines and protocols authoritative 'best practice'?

Scally and Donaldson's article appeared in July 1998. My criticism of it was published in December 1998, and mine was not the only critical voice (Smith & Harris 1999). Yet an article specially commissioned from Donaldson, which appeared in the summer 1999 issue of the *Journal of the Medical Defence Union* (Donaldson 1999), cited no critical articles, and made no effort to answer the worries that had been aired. Despite continuing informal reassurance that 'sorting out bad doctors' was only a small part of clinical governance, one third of Donaldson's article was concerned with 'Poor clinical performance'. In November 1999, I attended a conference on clinical governance at which Professor Donaldson's presentation yet again made no mention of any criticisms.

Professor Donaldson eventually responded to some of my worries in a later exchange of views in the same journal (Goodman & Donaldson 2000). He referred to the National Clinical Governance Support Team, which had been established in the meantime, and which should be helpful to trusts trying to get clinical governance to work. He did not convince me by his reply that clinical governance, in the form taken by his hexagon (see above), has a sound foundation, and clearly I am more worried than he is by the distorting effects of the media.

Is there anything of substance in clinical governance?

Scally and Donaldson's article was largely based on platitude (that we should provide quality in medical care), and took a lot of sometimes poorly chosen words to state the obvious, but their summary points (despite question-posing phrases such as 'positive organisational cultures') are worth some thought.

1. Clinical governance is to be the main vehicle for continuously improving the quality of patient care and developing the capacity of the NHS in England to maintain high standards (including dealing with poor professional performance).
2. It requires an organisation-wide transformation; clinical leadership and positive organisational cultures are particularly important.
3. Local professional self-regulation will be the key to dealing with the complex problems of poor performance among clinicians.

4. New approaches are needed to enable the recognition and replication of good clinical practice to ensure that lessons are reliably learned from failures in standards of care.

Clinical governance is whatever its authors decided it will be. In my view, they have tried too hard to make it all things to all people. For that reason, although some improvements will undeniably happen because of clinical governance, it is inevitable that, as a whole, it will fail. What will we do then? Good leadership will not come because we're told we need it. And if you want all this to happen, it's better to give the staff the resources and time to get on with it, and trust them to do it, than to take every opportunity, as the politicians seem to do, of accusing them of being 'forces of conservatism' standing in the way of the 'modernisation' of the NHS. As a *New Statesman* editorial put it, the present habit of the government is to hand out funds grudgingly, under stringent rules and controls for fear of waste and what it calls 'poor value', and then complain that the public sector lacks enterprise and innovation (Anonymous 1999). Specifically on doctors, an essayist wrote that 'Doctors are intelligent people, who have generally worked hard ... . Increasingly, they are being treated as if they were criminally inclined and stupid into the bargain, in need of the superior wisdom of the government to keep them in order' (Dalrymple 1999).

Unfortunately, it is difficult to disentangle clinical governance from politics. Hopkins (2000) wrote that we shouldn't dismiss the fundamental ideas behind developments such as clinical governance and the National Institute for Clinical Excellence just because of the political packaging. But the fundamental ideas *are* political. People have tried to expand and explain what is meant by clinical governance, but they tend to get bogged down in platitudes. *Hospital Medicine* published a series of articles between July 1999 and January 2000, (see the introductory editorial (Heard 1999)), which provides much fun for the reader wishing to count the number of times 'culture change', 'quality service', and 'evidence-based' appear. In my view, the best of this series is by Gilmore (2000), but in one article of the series Thomas (1999) writes that 'there is no mileage in carping from the sidelines – the world has moved on – openness, transparency and public accountability are here to stay'. There may not be mileage, and we should not carp, but we must continue to question. The world may find that too much openness, transparency and public accountability make it a worse, not a better, place (Smith 1995).

The wider picture

Cynicism about clinical governance does *not* imply an objection to quality in medicine, or that we should not strive to do the best for our patients, not just as we see it but as our patients see it. But the delivery of healthcare is complicated, so complicated that there are no easy solutions, no curative big ideas. There will always be problems and strains within the service. It would have been enough for Scally and Donaldson to have announced the end of the age of competition within the NHS, asked us and allowed us to collaborate for better healthcare, and given us encouragement: 'people work best if they are given a worthwhile job and are allowed to get on with it.' (Owen 1995).

The most important elements in the delivery of quality in healthcare are contained in the relations between human beings: doctor and patient, doctor and doctor, doctor and manager, manager and porter, occupational therapist and client. With good working relationships, clinical governance (or whatever it's called) happens naturally; with poor working relationships, setting up committees and defining quality on pieces of paper delivers nothing but pieces of paper. You can write *descriptions* of human behaviour, but it is more difficult to write rules to *govern* human behaviour. It is deceptive to think that when faults are found in a service, the faults can be corrected by measuring more and more closely what the service providers do.

In my essay, I asked the question "By what comparisons is overall quality in the NHS unsatisfactory?" I never received an answer to this, but the winter of 1999–2000 and its aftermath provided it. The biggest problem with the NHS is not that it doesn't *try* to deliver the best it can, but that it *cannot* deliver the best that it can. Clinical governance is a distraction. I am not convinced that the emperor's embarrassment will be spared.

References

Anonymous (1999). Now repair the window frames. *New Statesman* **2**, 4

Dalrymple T (1999). Who will rid us of these meddling managers? *New Statesman* **25**, 32–33

Department of Health (1997). *The new NHS: Modern and Dependable*. London: The Stationery Office

Donaldson L (1999). Clinical governance – medical practice in a new era. *Journal of the Medical Defence Union* **15**, 7–9

Frankel S, Sterne J, Davey Smith G (2000). Mortality variations as a measure of general practitioner performance: implications of the Shipman case. *British Medical Journal* **320**, 489

Gilmore I (2000). Clinical governance: what it is, what it isn't and what it should be. *Hospital Medicine* **61**, 51–53

Goodman NW (1998). Clinical governance *British Medical Journal* **317**, 1725–1727

Goodman NW (2000a). Accountability, clinical governance and the acceptance of imperfection. *Journal of the Royal Society of Medicine* **93**, 56–58

Goodman NW (2000b). NICE and the new command structure: with what competence and with what authority will evidence be selected and interpreted for local clinical practice? In Miles A, Hampton JR, Hurwitz B (eds) *NICE, CHI and the NHS Reforms: Enabling Excellence or Imposing Control?* London: Aesculapius Medical Press. pp33–50

Goodman NW & Donaldson L (2000). Clinical governance – an exchange of views. *Journal of the Medical Defence Union* **16**, 14–15

Heard S (1999). Clinical governance: opportunity or Pandora's box? *Hospital Medicine* **60**, 470–471

Hopkins PM (2000). A shame about the patient? *British Journal of Anaesthesia* **84**, 1–2
Owen AV (1995). Getting the best from people. *British Medical Journal* **310**, 648–651
Parry GJ, Gould CR, McCabe CJ *et al.* (1998). Annual league tables of mortality in neonatal intensive care units: longitudinal study. *British Medical Journal* **316**, 1931–1935
Pollock AM & Dunnigan MG (2000). Beds in the NHS. *British Medical Journal* **320**, 461–462
Rothwell PM, Warlow CP *et al.* (1999). Danger of misinterpretation of unusually high or low risks. *Lancet* **353**, 1325
Scally G & Donaldson IJ (1998). Clinical governance and the drive for quality improvement in the new NHS in England. *British Medical Journal* **317**, 61–65
Signorini DF & Weir NU (1999). Any variability in outcome comparisons adjusted for case mix must be accounted for [letter]. *British Medical Journal* **318**, 128
Smith P (1995). On the unintended consequences of publishing performance data in the public sector. *International Journal of Public Admininistration* **18**, 277–310
Smith LFP & Harris D (1999). Clinical governance – a new label for old ingredients: quality or quantity? *British Journal of General Practice* **49**, 339–340
Stark J, Gallivan S, Lovegrove J *et al.* (2000). Mortality rates after surgery for congenital heart defects in children and surgeons' performance. *Lancet* **355**, 1004–1007
Thomas H (1999). Clinical governance and revalidation. *Hospital Medicine* **60**, 892–896
Walshe K (2000). Clinical governance [letter]. *British Medical Journal* http://www.bmj.com/cgi/eletters/317/7174/1725

Chapter 9

Local systems of clinical governance and the role of annual appraisal, retraining and revalidation: three mechanisms of government control via the NHS and GMC

Brian Ayers

In December 1997 the government introduced new initiatives to stimulate clinical quality assurance in the National Health Service by announcing the development of some new national committee/organisations and by stimulating renewed interest in a range of local activities to promote the quality of patient care. Clinical governance refers to the local arrangements to support this national thrust for clinical quality in the NHS and is the basis of three government papers produced to support the initiative (Figure 9.1).

The new NHS:
modern and dependable December 1997

A First Class service:
Quality in the new NHS June 1998

Clinical Governance:
Quality in the new NHS HSC 1999/065

Figure 9.1 The new NHS

> The new NHS will have quality at its heart. Without it there is unfairness. Every patient who is treated in the NHS wants to know that they can rely on receiving high quality care when they need it. Every part of the NHS and everyone who works in it should take responsibility for working to improve quality.

Since 1997 there has been a plethora of meetings across the country to promote the clinical care aspects of clinical governance and their monitoring, but this quotation also refers to the timeliness of treatment. It makes no specific reference to waiting lists, but clearly there is an inference in the quotation that patients should be able to receive treatment on request, rather than at the convenience of the constituent parts of the health service. The Government's documents refer to ways in which the NHS expects trusts to maintain high clinical standards. Many of these mechanisms will be used in hospitals up and down the country already, but the stimulus from the clinical governance initiative was to examine one's own position (Figure 9.2).

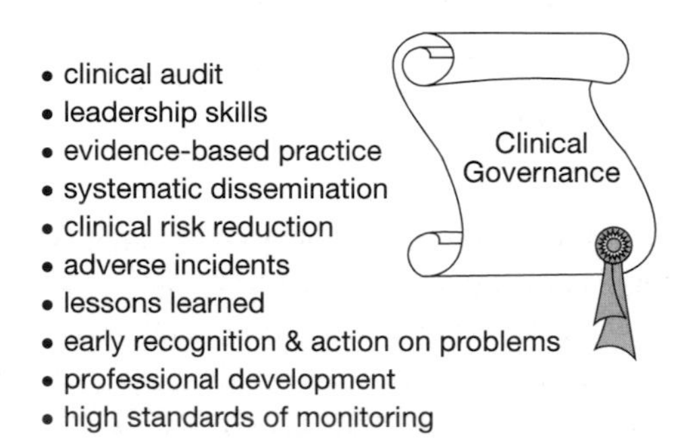

Figure 9.2 Principal elements of clinical governance

Figure 9.2 shows the elements of clinical governance described within the government papers and Figure 9.3 demonstrates those areas of activity which were, for example, already in use at Guy's & St Thomas' Hospital Trust in 1998. The clinical management arrangements at Guy's & St Thomas' include a well developed system of clinical directorates, which we believe is an important cornerstone in the maintenance of high standards, and we have relied heavily on individual clinical directors to ensure that directorate standards were high. The clinical governance initiative stimulated us to analyse the performance of individual directorates. Previously, there had been no regular central monitoring of clinical performance, but now under clinical governance each clinical director will have particular responsibility to ensure that their directorates are active in all the areas specified.

The initiative brought with it not only a stimulus to look at clinical practice but requirements for changes in the managerial responsibility of clinical care. Trust boards now have a responsibility, through their chief executive, for clinical quality. Why should they take these additional responsibilities seriously? Firstly, of course, as managers within the NHS, chief executives will need to be able to demonstrate that their responsibilities for governance in general are being met, and now this includes clinical activity. The principles are referred to in the 1992 Cadbury report on corporate governance. The responsibility of trust boards, their directors and in particular the chief executive is to ensure that monitoring mechanisms exist to interrogate internal controls for maintaining standards. This is also covered by

Guy's & St Thomas'

- Clinical directorates
- Focus on quality committee
- Clinical risk management group
- Clinical audit
- Education and training – PD programmes
- Complaints procedures
- Drugs and therapeutics committee

Figure 9.3 Established mechanisms for maintaining the quality of patient care at Guy's and St Thomas' Hospital Trust

another NHS document related to controls assurance – HSC(97)17. Through these mechanisms, trust boards are expected to be accountable to the public and to fulfil this obligation by producing an annual report for public scrutiny. It is generally accepted that not only will this document contain an outline of the mechanisms that a trust uses to ensure high standards of clinical care and high standards of monitoring of that care, but that in time it may also include specific details of individual consultant performance.

The national elements of the government's initiative must also be remembered in relation to local clinical governance. The National Institute for Clinical Excellence, and the National Service Frameworks are in the process of setting out for trust boards the services that the government of the day believe are the priorities for attention and investment (or retraction) and within these what standards can be expected by patients. The Commission for Health Improvement has now been constituted and is in the preliminary activity of identifying how it will examine the clinical quality performance of trusts. As yet it is not clear how national patient and user surveys will be used to feed into this system. The figure demonstrating these relationships will now be familiar to a large number of people – Figure 9.4 – but what will happen if locally there is no response? The implications, and indeed the threats, are that if the local trust takes little notice of this initiative, then their ability to set their own priorities of service care will be taken over by the national institutions and local managers and clinicians will be subject to severe scrutiny and control (Figure 9.5). Changes in the management and improvements in performance can be achieved by this sort of mechanism, but good management teaching suggests that it is also useful to produce benefits for institutions and management when seeking compliance with new initiatives. However, it is extremely difficult to identify any 'carrots' that are related with the clinical governance initiative.

The new Health Bill giving legal empowerment to this initiative states that there is a statutory duty of quality that balances the National Health Service's duties in financial areas. Clinical governance and financial governance are now on an equal footing. The financial standard of an annual balanced budget, which trusts are

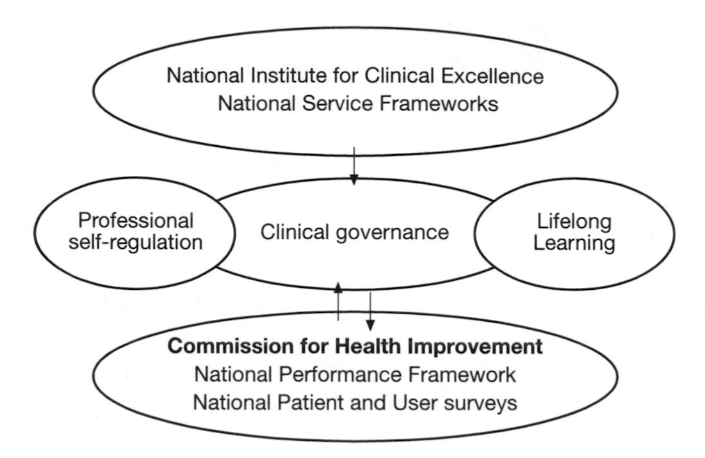

Figure 9.4 Principal relationships of clinical governance showing its central role position – the official version

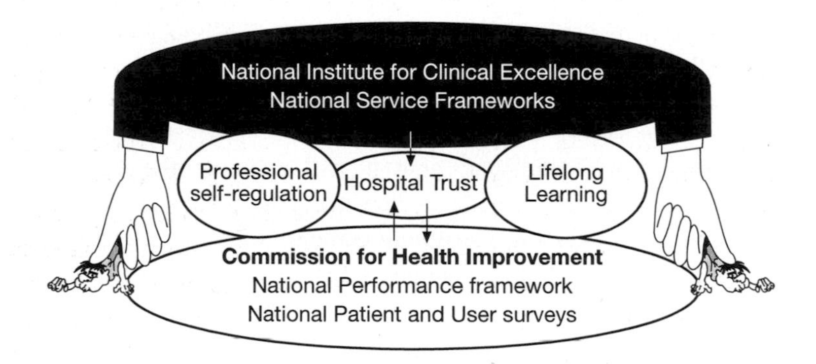

Figure 9.5 The restricting effects of central control. Compare with Figure 9.4

expected to work to, is an internationally recognised standard. What is the equivalent standard for clinical practice? It seems to me that it is certainly not a 12-month waiting list for cardiac surgery. Where, then, does this question lead us? In setting standards one has to accept that there is no such thing as an absolute standard within clinical practice. The standards that are expected within the NHS can be seen through a number of different eyes. Clinical professional staff will have standards of their own, which are developed over many years of training, and by their own motivation and conscience. The trusts, which clinical staff work for, may wish to set their own standards for their employees to meet, and these may reflect also, or not, the standards which the local purchasers wish to set for the patients for whom they are responsible. At a national level organisations such as the General Medical Council and the UKCC in its current and future form may wish to set standards of professional performance, and thereby clinical care of patients, which represent a minimum for all staff registered with those organisations. Other professional bodies, such as the Medical Royal Colleges, have standards that they expect their Fellows and Members to comply with. In the past, these have been by implication or by peer pressure, but the trend in recent years has been for these to be more specifically stated within publications from the Colleges.

To a large extent all the above standards are contained within the profession and are little understood outside professional staff. This may well apply to a number of managerial staff within the National Health Service, but certainly when one reads the wide variety of articles that now appear in the newspapers and are relayed on radio and television, it is clear that the press have different standards which are quite variable. There are also various groups of the public who, representing particular issues, set standards that they believe are reasonable for their particular group, without much consideration of the achievability of these standards within the totality of the health service that is expected to be provided. Governments follow governments and the standards of clinical performance in the National Health Service will follow the philosophy and standards set by government ministers. The new beneficial finance on offer for the health service at the moment carries with it central expectations of a change in performance. This does not necessarily mean that the finances, although welcome, are going to be useful to face some of the challenges that the health service is facing at the current time. It is not available to solve old problems that are not part of the priorities being set by the government.

And finally, of course, there is the patient. Those of us in clinical practice know that patient expectations vary enormously. Some of the most poorly treated patients, in my experience, are the most grateful, and the reverse applies whereby some patients who, in my view, have received the complete attention of staff and have been provided with the most up-to-date treatment are the most critical, and most disappointed. But, at the end of the day, the National Health Service, and those of us who work within it, are there to provide a service to patients. This is not just an idealistic philosophy, but a practical concept in relation to the funding of the National Health Service through taxation.

Over the last few years, during which clinical governance has been introduced, the General Medical Council has also been taking new powers from Parliament to address the poor performance of doctors that has been the focus of so much media attention in the last two years. The General Medical Council came into existence during the century before last, in order to set the standards of undergraduate education of doctors, and through the maintenance of a Medical Register to give a higher level of guarantee to the public that practising doctors have been well trained. Registration takes into account basic qualifications to practise obtained through training programmes of the universities. The standards of undergraduate education are monitored through the universities and through the General Medical Council. These responsibilities continue into the pre-registration house job year, but further standards of training and education are set by other bodies, such as the medical Royal Colleges. Under the new poor performance procedures, poorly performing doctors are defined as those whose registration is potentially in question. The GMC's interest in maintaining an active register lies mainly with the clinical requirement for basic practice, but the specialty register also requires confirmation from the appropriate college of an individual's training and capability. These matters are dealt with by the Fitness to Practise Division within the General Medical Council, which has three main elements – health, conduct, and poor performance. The health procedures are private and confidential and aimed to be remedial. If the doctor co-operates, the matter will be handled entirely locally and confidentially. The conduct procedures on the other hand are formal, public and adversarial. They are designed to deal with specific incidents, but do not allow the GMC to investigate a doctor's general standard of practice. There are no provisions for formal counselling, retraining or re-assessment where there is evidence of continuing poor performance. The conduct procedures can be used to investigate particular serious incidents, and may lead to removal of registration. They are not designed to investigate patterns of poor performance. The new poor performance procedures have been developed to fill this gap, and are designed to protect the public, and at the same time to give the deficient doctor the chance to improve. The procedures are designed to use reports of concerns about a doctor's performance to make a wide-ranging assessment, which considers all aspects of an individual doctor's practice and does not just focus on the complaints that have led to the concerns. In introducing these procedures, much debate has taken place as to the standards to which the GMC should be working. Clearly, many doctors will have long passed their university training programmes and the debate moves into the question of re-accreditation or revalidation of doctors, who have been in practice for some considerable time. Previously in this chapter I have referred to the many different parties interested in setting standards for professional performance in the National Health Service and these are also to be satisfied, as far as possible, with any programme for revalidation. It is hoped that any system of revalidation will provide the patient and the public at large with the confidence to continue to see their medical practitioners with the knowledge that high standards of clinical care will be available.

The British Association of Medical Managers has produced a definition of revalidation, which it is helpful to consider: 'Specialists and general practitioners must be able to demonstrate, on a regular basis, that they are keeping up-to-date and remain fit to practise in their chosen field'. This statement indicates the emphasis on the responsibility of individual professionals to maintain their own standards, and to be able to demonstrate this in a transparent and open manner. A university degree in medicine from 20 years ago does not give the reassurance that the doctor is performing appropriately now. The General Medical Council, in my view, is not in a position to make that judgement in relation to every single doctor's practice in this country, and revalidation will require local consideration of the concept of 'fitness for purpose'. It is unreasonable to make judgements over the lack of an ability of a doctor to perform a particular task, if that is not part of his working life. From a trust's point of view, the question for fitness to practise is part of performance management of clinical staff. In setting the performance expected of clinical staff, trusts, as employers within a common National Health Service, will be expected to take into account the standards expected from all the bodies that have been discussed previously. Many trusts will have currently informal mechanisms for performance management of consultant staff, as indicated in Figure 9.2, but until recent years few have developed formal systems of annual appraisal. Within the Guy's & St Thomas' Hospital Trust, the mechanisms that have been in existence for some time include a devolved clinical directorate system of clinical management, in which consultants are expected to undertake the duties of a clinical director responsible for management of areas of practice within the trust. Within these responsibilities, the expectation of monitoring the performance of immediate colleagues was implied, but recent pressures have made it necessary to make this a clear and specific responsibility. The trust has always been involved in clinical audit but, without systematic monitoring, this has been developed more in some areas of clinical practice than in others. It is now a requirement that all consultants be involved in clinical audit, and the clinical governance requirement is that the trust should be able to monitor this activity and to demonstrate to its own and to external satisfaction that this process is effective in maintaining standards of patient care. Within the process of transparency and documentation, which are the main themes around us at present, the value of professional meetings is grossly underestimated. As a radiologist, I am kept on my toes professionally by the regular clinical meetings I have with clinical colleagues, and with my own peers within radiology. Those weekly meetings where cases are presented with the answers to be given after I have stated my opinion on the available images are very demanding and soul searching. In my own experience, comments made at those meetings are more likely to drive me to the library to look up references and to renew my knowledge of particular topics, than other forms of embarrassment or managerial pressure.

In response to interests generated from such public events as the Bristol case, many trusts have set up standards committees to which concerns of staff and patients, not satisfied by the responses of clinical management, can be referred. The multidisciplinary Clinical Standards Committee at Guy's & St Thomas' Hospital Trust fulfils this function and is instituted to monitor the trust's progress towards the ideals of clinical governance.

Consultants' performance is rewarded in many different ways, but there is a national organisation of reward of distinction awards, that carry substantial remuneration. The old 'C' award system has been replaced by a more locally-based system of discretionary points. This system encourages consultants to improve their performance, and requires consultants to fill in a curriculum vitae questionnaire on a regular basis, should they wish consideration. However, the system fails to address poor performance if found through this mechanism. At Guy's & St Thomas' Hospital Trust we began a system of annual review for consultants some four years ago, that combines a review of the job plan with appraisal and continuous professional development. Consultant reviews are undertaken by their respective clinical directors or in the case of university staff by the heads of division. The same system is used for clinical staff, whether employed by the trust or by the university. These reviews are linked to the trust's annual planning cycle, are timetabled in advance and training is provided for the clinical directors. It is expected that clinical directors address the question of 'fitness for purpose' of consultants, as well as dealing with contractual issues. However, it is emphasised that serious contractual issues should be addressed outside this performance review. This system is not an excuse for postponing serious managerial matters. It is a requirement of employment within the trust that consultants undergo this annual review. Accepting that consultants are unlikely to accept such a simple dictat from on high, the timetabling of the reviews are clearly linked to the processes within the trust for assessing consultants for distinction awards and discretionary points. It is an accepted principle within the trust that consultants will not be considered for either reward scheme if an annual review has not been completed satisfactorily. The principles of the hour-long annual interview are explained both to the consultants and to the clinical directors, and it is made clear that only 20 per cent of the time should be used to address issues involved in assessment of performance and the rest of the time should be used in appraisal and planning to meet career aspirations. It is recognised that this is a longterm educational process and full benefit will only be achieved when the appraisees are confident that it is a beneficial process for them, as well as for their directorate and patients. The essential features we have tried to introduce are that the annual review is for everybody (92 per cent compliance was obtained in 1999/2000); that the same process is used for all staff so that there is no variation between directorates; a positive outcome must be achieved for all consultants by agreement and this should lead to further training opportunities. The paperwork has been designed to be clear and easy to use, although not all consultants will agree that these aims have been achieved. Consultants are encouraged, not only to define their basic working week to satisfy contractual requirements, but to use the opportunity to describe their professional life. The objectives of the review meeting are made clear before the event and are summarised in Figure 9.6. We believe that these annual reviews will form a solid basis for revalidation and will need to be honed to the central requirements currently under discussion and for the development of individual portfolios. I also believe that in addition to the annual reviews as described, there will be a need to identify some other indicators of performance. These may include objective tests of competence, as could be provided by clinical skills laboratories, or of input from colleagues outside the clinical directorate and also by patients. All the job plan reviews within our Trust are scrutinised by the Clinical Dean and by the Medical Director, which gives some element of objective peer review, but I suspect other elements will need to be introduced to satisfy the external scrutiny and to fulfil a national revalidation programme.

- agree fixed, flexible and external commitments
- review leave records
- discuss performance and identify best practice
- identify the organisation's needs and strategy
- identify training and development needs
- create a personal development plan
- discuss long term career aspirations and needs

Figure 9.6 Objectives of review meeting

Colleagues and peers have an input into one's individual performance assessment and appraisal in a number of different ways, whether they be clinical directors or not. Through clinical audit one's colleagues provide a benchmark by which to compare oneself. I have previously mentioned the stimulus of professional meetings, but within those meetings as peers we are forming judgements of our colleagues' abilities, competence, and performance. Whistle-blowing mechanisms exist whereby concerns can be raised, even anonymously if necessary, through such organisations as our Clinical Standards Committee. In a teaching environment, colleagues can be extended to include students, whether these be medical students or not, and currently within our Trust, final year medical students are used to undertake audits of communication skills and of note-keeping on behalf of the Trust and thereby are providing evidence on which judgements of clinical performance can be based. Colleagues can also be valuable in providing information through questionnaires.

However, at the end of the day, we must satisfy our patients, and we may involve patients as the GMC does as advisers to the development of procedures for assessment of poor performance, i.e., as assessors of the processes, but they should also be involved as peers in making judgements on individual performance. At present this activity is mainly limited to those members of the public chosen by respective bodies as sensible people. However, any member of the public can provide information on the performance of doctors through complaints procedures and indeed by providing compliments. It is to me a lost opportunity that the clinical governance initiative has laid so much emphasis on learning lessons from complaints, rather than learning lessons from compliments or plaudits. Patients are also available for providing information through questionnaires. I am particularly attracted by the American Board of Internal Medicine re-certification programme, including a self-evaluation process. In this process not only is the practising doctor asked to provide a self-evaluation of basic requirements, but this is supplemented by professional associated ratings (PARs) from 20 colleagues and patient satisfaction questionnaires (PSQs) from 50 patients. The colleagues and patients are selected by the individual practitioner and their replies are received on an automated telephone system (request@abim.org or www.abim.org). I believe this system tested on colleagues in the United States may well form the basis of a more in depth periodic assessment of consultant performance to supplement annual appraisal processes for revalidation.

Chapter 10

On clinical un-liberty: analysing the notion of clinical governance and constructing guiding principles

Carl Onion

Phase 1 – analysis

Clinicians under scrutiny

The UK government promotes clinical governance as an overarching mechanism designed to improve clinical quality in the National Health Service (NHS). It is defined as, 'A framework through which NHS organisations are accountable for continuously improving the quality of their services and safeguarding the high standards of care by creating an environment in which excellence in clinical care will flourish.' To establish clear guidance on best practice, a National Institute for Clinical Excellence (NICE) has been created to 'give new coherence and prominence to information about clinical and cost effectiveness'. A Commission for Health Improvement (CHI) has been established to 'offer an independent guarantee that local systems to monitor, assure and improve clinical quality are in place'. The Commission has powers, for example, to remove NHS chairpersons and non-executive directors where there is evidence of systematic failure (Department of Health 1998a).

Through clinical governance, practice consistent and practice inconsistent with NICE's recommendations will be thrown into stark relief: and where deemed appropriate the statutory CHI will call errant doctors and their organisations to account.

Clinical governance is a direct challenge to clinical freedom. What does this mean? Does it matter? Is it a good thing? Does it represent good or bad intentions? How should doctors respond?

Freedom to serve

Clinical freedom is a cherished medical notion and is an expression of the individual doctor's liberty to practise as he sees fit. Clinical freedom is, in essence, being at liberty to avail oneself of any relevant clinical option. The justification for clinical freedom is the unfettered pursuit, by the doctor, of the patient's best interests.

The free doctor's success, and the fate of his patient, is dependent upon his personal acumen and awareness. It is incumbent on the free doctor constantly to observe the practice of his colleagues and to review his practice in the light of published evidence to ensure his practice does not become adrift from reasonable practice over time. The motivation for perpetual review is fear caused by uncertainty over the current validity of the knowledge, skills and beliefs he holds. Unfortunately, some doctors have not observed this duty and the quality of their work has slipped unacceptably, hence the call for clinical governance.

The free doctor will wish, for the sake of security, to reference his practices to those of his colleagues generally – to observe 'common practice'. However, if his colleagues apply the process in reverse they will tend to condemn any 'aberrant' practices of his as incorrect, simply because they are different. In Bertrand Russell's example, the man who thinks he is a poached egg will be considered in error simply because he doesn't happen to hold the majority view (Russell 1912). There is thus considerable peer pressure to conform. We can expect that greater openness and sharing of performance data among clinicians would enhance the peer pressure effect and enhance conformity, regardless of the availability of clinical guidelines.

Natural liberty

The sixteenth century English physician and philosopher, John Locke, convinced of the intrinsic good in people, thought liberty represented a social paradise of altruism and self-fulfilment (Wooton 1993). While to the political philosopher Thomas Hobbes, with a perhaps more practical view of people within society, complete freedom would simply lead to a 'solitary, poor, nasty, brutish and short' life (Gaskin 1996). Despite much subsequent philosophical to-ing and fro-ing down the ages it is clear that there is truth in both sides of the argument. In the medical context therefore, clinical freedom, like any other freedom, must deliver both some benefits and some harm. If the harms outweigh the benefits, then freedom should be curtailed as appropriate.

I stand out, therefore I am outstanding

There is a tension in the expression of individualism. To Kierkegaard and subsequent existentialists the individual is more important than the collective view (Connell 1991). So, whether your being a good doctor is a good thing to society or not is immaterial, what matters is whether it is a good thing to you. Communities following the Sartre line that to exist one must express individuality 'for itself' (Warnock 1972), collide with the paradox that to be accepted as the same, one must be seen to be different. And there is the danger that freedom to express individuality may be exercised for its own sake or to gain favour. In medical society, such a philosophy may be observed among practitioners eager to show how they are different in order to attract clients.

Kierkegaard also anticipated the authors of clinical guidelines in his description of academics with an ability to develop magnificent and perfect palaces built on reason and evidence, but who live outside in a shed (Connell 1991). Those who counsel perfect practice must remain aware that they are not even capable of this themselves.

Who should have the final say?

There is a danger that the doctor's individuality is expressed at the expense of his patient's freedom. The remedy to this is patient empowerment where the patient is also enabled to express his individual preferences. Whose preferences should prevail? Liberty dictates, at first glance, the patient's authority. However, St Luke's thought provoking question *'quis maior est, qui recumbit an qui ministrat?'* (Who is more important, he who dines or he who serves? – St Luke xxii, 27) leads us perhaps to conclude that the doctor may be equally important. Certainly, while not riding roughshod over the patient's preferences, the doctor should not endorse the patient's individual view when it will put health in peril.

Liberty and society

In any social context, the expression of personal liberty to its fullest extent will impinge upon the liberty of others. In an NHS context, the doctor considering only the interests of the patient before him and using scarce referral or treatment or special investigation without discretion is using up the resources available to other patients, thereby reducing the options open to them. Victorian liberal JS Mill proposed that exercise of personal liberty, while of primary importance, is not sufficient warrant for impinging upon the liberty of others (Himmelfarb 1974). Mill's views have left their influence on modern British politics of all major persuasions.

A tension foreseen by Mill in any democracy based upon majority voting is the subordination of the needs of minorities to those of the majority. In a medical context, patients with unusual or stigmatised diseases or circumstances do not tend to have their needs addressed as well as those patients with common diseases or those whose diseases attract public sympathy – a tyranny of the majority. Examples would be controversies around allocating resources to HIV/AIDS, drugs misuse and alcoholism or the reluctance of Primary Care Group boards to divert funds from able practices to prop up the minority of 'failing' practices or practices struggling to cope in demanding localities. Rightly and properly, politically driven National Service Frameworks will address problems faced by the majority of the population. But who is looking out for patients with unusual conditions?

Continuing professional will

To express one's individualism requires an exercising of one's will. To Arthur Schopenhauer, the will expresses itself through desires, longings, wants and cravings – a miserable dissatisfaction with our lot (Hamlyn 1980). We are driven to great lengths over long periods of time to satisfy the will, and yet, ironically, when we succeed our joy is fleeting and quickly makes way for another craving. The tedious pursuit of medical qualifications and the brief sense of success upon qualification will be familiar to the medical reader. Schopenhauer recommends asceticism as the antidote to the misery caused by our perpetual wants – a denial and consequent quietening of the will. Another answer, recommended in eastern philosophy, is to enjoy the labour and not the fruits of the labour – to enjoy the journey rather than the destination (Mascaró 1962). The modern doctor has to pursue continuing professional development and needs to learn to enjoy the learning experience for its own sake and not merely for the sake of acquiring factual knowledge – knowledge as a consequence of lifelong learning rather than its sole purpose. Medical knowledge is often out of date the moment it is acquired.

Übermedics

Nietsche describes 'overmen' (*übermensch*), a class of rare individuals with superior willpower who should naturally rise to positions of power and bend the masses to their will; they should not be bound by the 'herd' morality that applies to the rest of us (Hollingdale 1990). Those doctors who consider themselves in an elite class are liable to force their will on others. Perhaps these individuals will find their way into influential positions in medical politics, academic institutions, and the medical licensing authorities or into health services administrative posts and enforce their ideas in a top-down fashion. Those of us in elevated positions need to remind ourselves that we are there to help and not to dictate – unless, of course, we approve Nietsche's view.

Doctor knows best

To do what's best for people while respecting their autonomy requires, according to RM Hare, a third level of universalisability (Singer 1979). When we treat people how we think is best for them we have only achieved the first level – evidence-based medicine achieves this. Treating people as we would like to be treated if we were actually them nobly reaches the second level. However, to achieve the third level requires us to treat people as though we were them with their full set of personal beliefs, culture, social responsibilities, personality and aspirations. This is of course impossible … unless the patient is party to the decision-making. A doctor-patient partnership that empowers the patient to contribute to decision-making as fully as he is capable is the goal of the enlightened doctor (Onion 1997).

Survival of the unfittest

Darwin set a few, presumably unintended, political balls rolling with his biological thesis on survival of the fittest (Burrows 1982). Humans are, biologically, 'animals' and it did not take long for political thinkers to apply the same reasoning to cure weaknesses in society. At best this threw some light on the management of inherited diseases and the causes of the plight of the disadvantaged, at worse it 'excused' the worst excesses of genocide, including the involvement of doctors in merciless extermination policies enshrined in Nazi law (Redlich 1998). It has never been acceptable for doctors to claim they were 'just following orders' when implementing ethically flawed regulations or policies.

Similarly, simple Darwinism dictates that doctors should abandon sub-standard colleagues to their fate, but modern evolutionary thinking considers the species rather than the individual – even unfit or non-reproductive members can have a major positive impact on survival of a community (Dunbar 1992). Doctors unfit for their usual medical duties could be utilised in other ways within the bounds of their capabilities, but how often does this happen? Usually, full retirement on sickness grounds is the only option seriously considered and the individual's expertise is lost to society. Rules and regulations find unusual doctors inconvenient to accommodate.

Clinical disobedience

Doctors who wish to exhibit clinical freedom yet remain within the NHS system face a dilemma. Must they swallow their conscientious objections or resign? Socrates resolved a similar dilemma by inventing civil disobedience (Tredennik & Tarrant 1993). He concluded that he benefited from being a citizen of the state, and that if he felt morally obliged to contradict Athenian laws he should follow his conscience and then accept the state's appropriate penalty. Athens decided to execute him.

Scrutinising the scrutiny

Clinical governance is intended to produce manifold benefits, including the implementation of evidence-based medicine, greater harmony in NHS care provision and enhanced value for money. However, all good things come at a cost. Understandably, those intending to persuade us to embrace clinical governance tend to emphasise the credit side and play down the debit side in their account. Before we embark we need to reflect.

Perfect patients and patronising doctors

Patients clearly don't read medical textbooks or clinical guidelines. The one who does and exhibits classical symptoms and signs as he should, apart from being a suspect malingerer, is a *rara avis* that will attract hordes of medical students, be the focus of a case presentation and a major hold-up during the grand round. In this circumstance, where diagnosis is certain, the doctor is confident and appropriate treatment is exactly indicated, we would expect that the management is automatically appropriate. The doctor will give the patient what he needs according to guidance in the scientific literature.

But, even in a classic case, giving someone what you decide they need is patronising and disrespectful. No matter, the doctor is giving the patient what he, as a well-informed and clever doctor, would want if he were the patient. However, the doctor is poorly informed. Even if we ignore the uncertainties inherent in scientific knowledge, the doctor knows only a small part of the equation –the real expert is the patient. Only he knows his wants, his beliefs, his culture, his obligations, his plans, his family, his community, his motives. The enlightened doctor, in order to satisfy and achieve concordance with treatment and advice, collaborates with the patient to achieve fully informed decision-making. But, a guideline that establishes a script the doctor is obliged to follow must surely overpower, not empower the patient. The patronising doctor has made way for the patronising state.

Saved by the guideline

On the other hand, the patient with an unenlightened and ignorant doctor can benefit from clinical governance in that he is more likely to have evidence-based medicine applied to him – although he may, of course, have a guideline strictly applied to him when it does not apply!

Clinical guidelines and national policies liberate the clinician from anxiety over being out of step with the literature. The NHS doctor can use the national policies to restrain obstreperous patients. The NHS doctor not only speaks with the voice of NICE, but with the combined authority of all NHS doctors. The obedient NHS doctor can rest assured that a hierarchy – reaching from practice or directorate clinical governance leads, through primary care group or NHS trust clinical governance leads, and health authority clinical governance leads, to NICE and central government – will ensure the approach he adopts cannot be undermined by colleagues with different views. In parallel, a hierarchy from the accountable officers of NHS trusts, and health authorities through to the NHS executive and government will also ensure that compliance with the policies of NICE is maintained as a high priority for all those working in the NHS. Furthermore, there is an enforcement agency, the Commission for Health Improvement, which will ensure that organisations across the land all comply. The General Medical Council (GMC) and a new set of Assessment and Support Centres will have enhanced powers to pick off any stragglers or strugglers (Department of Health 1999a). Belt and braces, and more braces and yet another belt – which does suggest a feeling of insecurity about all these procedures.

Information use and misuse

Although many of us are willing to consider employing the occasional bad means to achieve a good end – for example, to tell a 'white' lie to save someone's feelings – we rarely feel good about it. St Thomas Aquinas maintained that it was never right to do bad things to achieve good things; we should pursue goodness in a goodly fashion (Glover 1977). Intuitively also, honour is more associated with those who have failed in virtuous pursuit of a cause than with those who succeeded in malicious pursuit of a good cause.

But how could clinical governance be misused? It is purely an educational means to develop better doctors and achieve good healthcare. Let us examine first the means, and then the ends.

In the UK there is a monopoly employer of doctors (the NHS) and one licensing authority (the GMC) – both run by government through the legislature. Doctors exercising proscribed clinical actions may face censure by both organisations with sanctions available such as suspension or removal from employment and loss of a licence to practise medicine anywhere in the UK. The new appraisal methodology devised by the GMC to examine 'doctors who give cause for concern' have been exacting ordeals even for those doctors who have nobly agreed to allow the device to be tested on them. No wonder doctors are feeling uneasy. Even slight over-enthusiasm in the use of the methodology of clinical governance or GMC appraisal could constitute bullying because of the overpowering nature of assessment procedures and the severity of potential penalties that profoundly affect the doctor's livelihood. The humane use of these new powers is entirely dependent upon the personalities and opinions of those in charge. One would particularly worry about a drift toward greater stringency over time.

A shot in the arm or self-shot in the foot

The public is likely to have sympathy with the victims of bad doctors, especially after a few high profile media exposés, and to support greater scrutiny and means of punishment of doctors. However, able young candidates are not likely to be attracted into an oppressive working environment and paradoxically members of the public may later find a shortage of high calibre medical care when they need it.

On the other hand, the new processes offer peer review, early detection of deteriorating standards of practice and early access to remedial education, occupational healthcare and continuing professional development. The doctor will only be encouraged to pursue practice that has been determined thoroughly and in good faith to be the best. The result must be a general improvement in medicine as poor and less well proven practices are eradicated.

Because NICE is obliged to take economic arguments into consideration and to justify the priority of its topics to government, there is a danger that the doctor may become an instrument to control the allocation of healthcare resources in accordance with governmental interests. Some doctors may find this role uncomfortable.

Automating medicine

As the gradual replacement of free medicine with approved medicine is accomplished ordinary doctors may find their work less stressful. Answers to clinical conundrums will be easily discovered by referring to a guideline, or automatically presented by the PRODIGY computer program (Sowerby Centre for Health Informatics at Newcastle 1998). There may be some problem accommodating the minority of patients who do not fit, but they have always received a raw deal from doctors (ask anyone with chronic fatigue syndrome) and at least they will be more clearly identified.

However, to do exactly as the computer bids, although it has its own rigour, is hardly intellectually demanding. Existing doctors will find interests outside their mainstream work to keep themselves stimulated. And it is likely that a different, less flamboyant breed could be attracted into medicine in the future. For variation, while a nuisance to administrators and concealing sub-optimal practices, also allows the human spirit to flourish in somewhat intangible ways. I suspect that we will only be aware of what we have lost when it has gone.

Organ-grinders and monkeys

It is clear that our governmental and academic masters want to see universal concordance with best practice as identified by a single excellent institute. But what do practising doctors want? Medical science has helped support medical practice, providing insights and facts and technologies to help the doctor in the perennial pursuit of caring for his patients. With clinical governance enforcing academic evidence-based medicine there is the beginning spectacle of a tail wagging a dog. Ordinary doctors must decide what they require, and do not require, from clinical governance and make their requirements known; otherwise they will receive what the scientist and economist ordered rather than what bits the doctor should have ordered.

Extinction of the nicest

If Darwinian theory applies, clinical governance will eradicate doctors unfit to practise and will facilitate the thriving of those fit to practise. However, biological excellence is not necessarily associated with survival. For example, the sabre-toothed cats were superbly and precisely designed to predate on the long-necked mega-herbivores of their time, but when these prey disappeared they were unable to adapt to other food sources (MacDonald 1993). Similarly, the medical technocrat purveying NICE's wares may easily survive clinical governance only to be abandoned by a public that seeks a more spiritual, flexible and caring health practitioner and personal advocate.

The NICE folk and the nasty

It is assumed that NICE will do its job properly and, with the confidence of a panel acting in good faith in the public interest, it will make its conclusions known explicitly and boldly. There will be times when its advice conflicts with the principles and interests of NHS staff members, their professional organisations, individual doctors, patients and their elected representatives. These conflicts must be well resolved for NICE to learn and healthcare to accommodate it.

The establishment of clear clinical guidelines based upon expert appraisal of evidence that the doctor is obliged to follow will hardly aid patient empowerment unless there is plenty of built-in scope for patient choice. David Eddy described an innovative US attempt that whittled the options down in the usual systematic review fashion until there were two or three options left to patient 'preference' (Eddy 1990). Unfortunately, the patient was merely allowed to make marginal decisions and the important decision making was left to the clever reviewers of the published evidence.

And what of the casualties, those who fail to make the grade? Unknowingly allowing bad practice to occur is bad enough, but when bad practitioners have been clearly exposed by a public body what then? Duty dictates that a NHS organisation cannot allow exposure of the public to a known dangerous doctor. But he may be considered remediable and so needs to be rehabilitated into service. Is it justifiable to endanger his first few patients so that others ultimately may benefit? The only solution is adequate supervision. This will come at a cost, both financially and in terms of intrusion into private consultations with patients. Better that supervision and attempted rehabilitation is not initiated at all than they be inadequate.

How sympathetically and positively will aberrant doctors be treated? The approaches taken will speak volumes on the humanity of the system, our profession and the public. If fallen colleagues were treated too harshly there would be a serious fall in medical morale. If treated too kindly, public confidence would be seriously affected. Which is the more important to our elected governors?

Phase 2 – constructing principles to govern clinical governance

Having examined some fundamental issues regarding the conflicting notions of clinical governance and clinical liberty, we must now derive some principles to guide our actions. In the face of inevitable implementation of clinical governance, the task at hand is to construct an approach to clinical governance that maximises its benefits and diminishes its harm. The following principles, in isolation, have also been published elsewhere (Onion 2000).

Promoting good practice

Clinical governance has been defined as, 'Corporate accountability for clinical performance' (Lee 1999). Examination of the official definition of clinical governance in the opening paragraph above reveals that clinical governance is intended to allow excellence to flourish and not directly to eradicate bad practice – although it may well contribute to its identification and could help with the rehabilitation process. 'Excellent practice' is practice based on systematic reviews of the relevant scientific evidence; this is not the same as 'good practice', it is a subset of good practice.

Clinical governance is a means to achieving compliance with one form of good practice

Clinical governance is increased corporate conformity with advice based on a systematic review of empirical evidence including an appraisal of cost-effectiveness – it is a form of good practice. Other forms of good practice include, rigorous scientific research, practice based on careful reasoning from basic principles and practice offering well-informed patients a wide range of choices.

It can be assumed that NICE will ably perform the function of assessing the evidence and will publish clear conclusions and summaries that will inform NHS clinicians and the commissioners of NHS services

NICE guidance is not absolute and cannot therefore identify bad practice with certainty. Similarly, the use of 'excellence' in the NICE title suggests that its recommendations represent *excellent* rather than *good* practice – something none of us could constantly match. Compliance would suggest good practice according to the criteria employed by NICE. In short, non-compliance does not equal bad practice. The question and answer section of the NICE website confirms this (National Institute for Clinical Excellence 1999):

> Will NICE in effect be a national rationing council/will NICE mean the end to clinical freedom?
>
> No. NICE will examine the evidence for the benefits and costs of new treatments and will give guidance to the NHS. But it will be for the individual commissioners and clinicians to decide on treatment in individual cases (sic).

NICE, in itself, will not mean an end to clinical freedom. NICE is charged only with developing national clinical guidelines, service frameworks and technology appraisals, but will play no part in operational implementation.

Those implementing clinical governance need to adopt a partnership approach with clinicians to achieve an acceptable balance between freedom and constraint as quickly and painlessly as possible

NHS Chief Executive Officers, Commissioners, and Clinical Governance Leads are charged with implementing the recommendations of NICE (Institute of Health Services Management 1999) – here is where clinical freedom's jeopardy lies. There will be a variation in the stringency of implementation of NICE recommendations among NHS officers, some will be too heavy-handed and will be resisted, some too delicate and will be ignored. Gradually, a level of application of guidelines that the doctors and their patients will tolerate will become apparent.

Implementation of NICE's guidance should be integrated into the continuing professional development (lifelong learning) arrangements of NHS staff

Mere dissemination of guidelines and isolated adoption in NHS service agreements (called Service and Financial Frameworks – SAFFs) will, of itself, achieve little (Onion & Walley 1998). An educational approach, akin to action learning, would allow teams of relevant professionals, clinical and non-clinical, to assess the local implications of NICE's pronouncements and determine what and how to implement locally.

Clinical guidelines reinforced by clinical governance will be particularly beneficial in care provided by multidisciplinary teams

Patients increasingly receive care from teams of healthcare workers rather than individual practitioners. In these circumstances, patients will benefit from receiving consistent approaches and messages from all their healthcare attendants (Department of Health 1998b).

All local public sector agencies with a significant interest should be played into clinical governance processes

Service changes need to be considered not only by the immediate commissioner and provider, but the views of those indirectly affected also need to be played in. This partnership approach (enshrined in local Health Improvement Plans) will include other NHS agencies (NHS Executive 1999), and other relevant local agencies like, for example, the local Social Services Department, the independent (voluntary) sector and patients/patients' representatives as appropriate to them.

Clinical governance should aim to establish conformity with discretion

Clinical governance, like corporate governance, is about individuals within an organisation adopting a unified approach, and greater consistency of approach between all organisations that constitute the NHS. That approach should be based upon evidence-based best practice and must be in the best interest of the organisation and those it serves. Unlike clinical audit, clinical governance is not about clinicians doing well what they want; it is about clinicians and their colleagues doing well what NICE wants. However, NICE guidance is intended to guide clinical judgement and it is appropriate to override the wishes of NICE, or even the patient's wishes, in occasional cases (Seedhouse 1988).

The NHS could construe habitual deviation from NICE guidance (or some similar valid source) as experimentation

If UK clinical governance goes the same way as US clinical policies, doctors will increasingly be required to explain deviations from NICE guidelines. If they have employed clinical judgement and decided on a different course of action then they will be readily able to justify their actions. However, if they decide to deviate wholesale from a NICE guideline they will need to have an equally credible referenced source of guidance, such as a guideline published by a Royal College. Provided that the deviating doctor can assemble a body of reasonable, like-minded colleagues he may feel protected from litigation by the Bolam test[1], which still appears valid (Hurwitz 1998). However, where clinicians wish to apply a different approach *Quality in the New NHS* (NHS Executive 1999) recommends rigorous comparative evaluation, presumably – if evidence-based medicine thinking is to be consistently applied – applying rigorous research methodology.

Persuasion to toe the corporate line may include the application of rewards or sanctions

Some non-compliant clinicians will be pursuing some other variety of good practices. Clinical governors will either have to tolerate their non-conformity or have to induce them to comply. It is imperative that these inducements are seen to be fairly applied.

Clinical governance can only change practice if extra resources are applied or existing resources are redirected

One thing is clear, clinical governance is about change. And change costs time, effort and money. NICE will prioritise its work to address topics where change is most required or where it is most possible. Change will be most required where there is a political, public health or fiscal imperative. Change will be most useful and achievable where new evidence is abundant, where dissatisfaction with current practice is widespread, or variation in practice is rampant.

Where clinical governance provokes an ethical conflict independent mediation should be attempted

Clinical governance demands a degree of conformity from NHS doctors. Doctors who 'believe' in the NHS on principle and who wish to continue to enjoy the benefits of NHS employment will, on occasion, have to swallow their conscientious objections. If a doctor really feels that an ethically unacceptable practice is being forced upon him, and is unable to resolve the conflict even through the use of an arbitrator or mediator, then he may feel that he would have to do what he thinks right and then face the consequences – a form of civil disobedience.

Combining existing quality and performance mechanisms will achieve the objectives of clinical governance most efficiently

The NHS organisations now have two principal duties. To prudent management of public funds has been added the responsibility for working to improve quality

---

1 'A doctor will not be guilty of negligence if he has acted in accordance with a practice accepted as proper by a responsible body of medical men skilled in that particular art.'

(Department of Health 1997). Clearly there is a tension between these two imperatives. However, there can be only one supreme principle – and it has to be the fiscal one (after all, everything has to be paid for). Despite this, it is clear that NHS organisations, within their financial constraints and facing increasing patient demand, are required to demonstrate continuously improved clinical performance. To achieve this will require the alignment of current relevant activities – including clinical audit, prescribing review, continuing professional development, information systems, risk management, and complaint procedures – within and between NHS agencies to address the overarching aims of clinical governance.

Synergy will be gained by working with others with overlapping goals

There is much overlap in the aims of NHS clinical governance and related performance processes and the aims of voluntary, commercial and other public sector organisations. Mutually beneficial partnerships should be encouraged.

Patients should be talked through all appropriate and relevant options, even those immediately unavailable on the NHS

The most important partnership is that with the individual patient. Some ways must be found to accommodate the individual patient's preferences: at the least, some sort of appeal process; at best an opportunity to weigh up the evidence with the doctor. Ultimately, if the option preferred by the patient is not within the gift of the NHS doctor to provide, this should be made explicit. The patient can then weigh up the new set of options that present; to go for private treatment, to accede to NHS will, to lobby his MP and so on.

Eradicating bad practice

It is interesting to note that clinical governance, in itself, will not remedy bad practice. New systems have been proposed to address bad medical practice and in particular to prevent 'a growing number of cases hitting the headlines' and consequent 'damage to public confidence in the ability of the National Health Service and the medical profession to deal with problem doctors quickly, effectively and fairly' (Department of Health 1999a). A governmental consultation paper proposes a third arm to assure medical quality: to clinical governance and the Commission for Health Improvement is to be added a system of assessment and support centres (Department of Health 1999b). The principles outlined below are relevant to the design and *modus operandi* of these recommended centres.

Clinical governance is designed to promote and ensure good practice. During its pursuit possible bad practice will be uncovered. Cases of suspected bad practice would also be identified from other sources. Systems to deal with bad practice should run in parallel with the system – clinical governance – to promote good practice. In this section some principles to govern the management of suspected bad practice are proposed and supported.

Most cases of bad practice will be identified by repeated aberrant behaviour, either in one aspect of practice or over several areas of practice

Bad practice (malpractice) is a category, or perhaps a ragbag, which contains miscellaneous sets of undesirable medical actions ranging from simple errors and misunderstandings through to sordid and criminal acts. The single unifying feature is actual or potential harm to others. Sometimes the harm is intended or the doctor is indifferent to the welfare of others, sometimes it is inadvertent or unforeseen. In either case the doctor may react with remorse or denial. And, in either case the doctor may be remediable or beyond redemption. Doctors giving cause for concern will be identified by either one spectacularly conspicuous episode of bad practice or, more usually, a pattern of repeated questionable practices detected by other professionals in their team, financial audit, customer complaints, and repeated dubious clinical performance highlighted through clinical governance or prescribing monitoring.

Some training and experience in the law, conflict resolution, medical jurisprudence or ethics are minimum requirements for those obliged to judge alleged malpractice and poor performance

Clearly, anyone dealing with malpractice has to make several fundamental and difficult judgements on the individual. The judges must be equipped to make and justify their judgements objectively.

Civil and criminal law are established and appropriate remedies in some cases of malpractice where damage is significant and an identifiable, careless individual is most likely at fault

When feeling threatened or wronged, people tend to identify a single culpable individual and to attack him. When it is appropriate, the adversarial British legal system is well suited to governing this approach.

Managerial expertise applied to an organisation will be the appropriate remedy in some cases of bad practice

Sometimes a more complex approach is required, particularly as multi-disciplinary teamwork becomes more commonplace in healthcare. Where malpractice is the result of systems failure rather than the fault of a single doctor, a managerial approach is more appropriate including a review of risk, human resource, operational, quality and information management as required.

Where education is deficient, postgraduate deans should be engaged to determine where deficiencies lie, how they might be addressed and to see that the resulting personal development plan is completed and evaluated

Frequently, malpractice is the result of gaps in current knowledge. Postgraduate deans and their staff are the source of expertise in determining weaknesses in knowledge and skills and in developing appropriate personal educational portfolios to overcome any deficiencies. Deans will already be calculating the cost of this emerging role.

Procedures employed to investigate alleged malpractice must be sensitive to physical, mental and social health issues affecting the doctor

Sadly, malpractice is commonly symptomatic of ill health or distress. Similarly, a doctor with sufficient insight to realise his inability to cope may feel hopeless. In some cultures, including the *macho* medical profession as a whole, admission of failure is not decorum. Clumsy application of correctional devices, such as clinical governance, will only aggravate matters. Because poor health may not be apparent when the malpractice is identified, it is important to maintain a supportive and positive disposition toward the doctor until the cause of the malpractice is determined with sufficient certainty.

Investigation of alleged malpractice must be positive and sympathetic

Even for those who have deliberately lapsed in their duty, the processes employed to investigate may cause anxiety out of all proportion to the magnitude of the misdemeanour.

Those investigating and managing alleged bad practice must resist punitive tendencies

There is a natural tendency to be angered when considering the suffering of victims of malpractice and to desire retribution. However, punishment is the jurisdiction of Crown appointed criminal law courts and tribunals alone.

Above all else, the purpose of all endeavours to address malpractice is to prevent future lapses in care

The purpose of addressing poor practice is to remedy where possible and to prevent always further malpractice.

In simple mishaps and misunderstandings skilled mediation may be required

Often malpractice is the result of isolated human error, unforeseen circumstances, failure of communication, misunderstanding or failure to meet unreasonable expectations. Both sides are likely to feel distressed, no blame is appropriate, but the doctor–patient relationship may have broken down. Clumsy handling may cause irretrievable damage to both parties and provoke fruitless pursuit of legal redress.

Local performance committees and the like must secure undertakings from the relevant agencies to guarantee the potentially necessary remedial resources before they commence proceedings

To eradicate bad practice will require investment in time and resources. If remedying of bad practice is not seen as a priority area for investment, the only available solutions to bad practices will be punitive, for example suspension or sacking.

Justifying the principles

DUCUNT VOLENTEM FATA, NOLENTEM TRAHUNT

(Lucius Annaeus Seneca, 4 BC to AC 65)

Original Latin emphasises the perennial validity of Seneca's words, 'Fate leads the willing, and drags the unwilling.'

For the UK, clinical governance is here to stay. It holds both promise and threat, and like all human developments is open to either use or abuse. For some it will resonate with strongly held views that corporate application of excellent practice is the noblest aspiration of a state-run National Health Service. For others, the inhibition of clinical freedom will stifle clinical practice, devalue clinical judgement, and adversely affect the doctor-patient relationship – in short, while a refined pedigree pleases dog show judges, mongrels make the healthiest pets.

Most of us, however, will see some merit in both extremes of the argument. We will attempt to gain the best of both worlds and lose the worse.

Compliance with clinical governance, while exacting, should guarantee a quieter life. Non-conformists will face pressure from their peers, management, patient groups and perhaps the law. Conformists will be able to dismiss criticism with the wave of a NICE guideline.

The explosion in medical knowledge and the eclectic nature of modern healthcare has undermined traditional beliefs in leaders and giants. With more teamwork and partnership in tackling ill health, corporate behaviour within and between disciplines becomes increasingly important. Clinical governance will help facilitate co-operative and concordant working practices and bring significant gains from the resulting concerted actions.

In theory, there is no need to tolerate non-conformity within clinical governance. In practice, tolerance will be essential. Clinical guidelines cannot foresee every patient's idiosyncrasies and preferences – there must be room for clinical judgement. Some clinicians will not have the right personality, or may have religious or moral objections to applying some aspects of a guideline. For example, despite perhaps having other strengths, they may not be very good at explaining things to patients. To drive them out of practice would be to lose the baby with the bath water. Clinicians trained abroad may have learned other approaches, it could be dangerous to compel them to follow unfamiliar clinical approaches.

A balance must be struck between clinical corporateness and clinical freedom. In fact, clinical governance represents a series of checks and balances. The recommendations of this chapter (Tables 10.1 and 10.2) will help to ensure that these balances are achieved in a way that maximises the potential for clinical governance.

The integration of personal lifelong learning with clinical governance will ensure that those who have to apply clinical guidelines are in an informed position to judge where the guidelines apply and where they do not.

Partnerships between clinicians and managers will promote successful implementation of guidelines by ensuring that service changes enable appropriate changes in practice.

Those convinced that there are better ways to treat conditions than those promoted in NICE guidelines should rigorously and scientifically evaluate their practice so that their evidence can be assimilated into the systematic review that leads to refining of guidelines over time.

Involvement of all relevant agencies in clinical guideline/service framework implementation will benefit all, not only from simple synergy, but also because all UK public bodies now face their own versions of performance governance.

The recommendations for tackling bad practice are valid whether clinical governance exists or not. However, clinical governance will be helpful in highlighting where bad practice might be occurring and as a basis for educational solutions.

There are so many chinks in the evidential and ethical armour of clinical governance that a profession mischievously inclined could run rings around it. However, this would be neither in the interests of NHS doctors nor their patients. Better that doctors work with clinical governance to allow its benefits to flourish and to check its potential for ill, and better that the NHS does not rigidly enforce it.

Clinical governance will make clinical decision making and resource allocation more effective and explicit for the NHS patient. However, this benefit will be achieved at a significant cost to patient and doctor liberty.

Table 10.1 Clinical governance – principles for promoting excellent practice

1. Clinical governance is a means to achieving compliance with one form of good practice.
2. It is assumed that NICE will ably perform the function of assessing the evidence and will publish clear conclusions and summaries that will in themselves, a) be useful to NHS clinicians wishing to keep up-to-date, and b) ensure the commissioning process is well informed.
3. Those implementing clinical governance should adopt a partnership approach with clinicians to achieve an acceptable balance between freedom and constraint as quickly and painlessly as possible.
4. Implementation of NICE's guidance should be integrated into the continuing professional development (lifelong learning) arrangements of NHS staff.
5. Clinical guidelines reinforced by clinical governance will be particularly beneficial in care provided by multidisciplinary teams.
6. All local public sector agencies with a significant interest should be played into clinical guideline and national service framework implementation.
7. Clinical governance should aim to establish conformity with discretion.
8. The NHS should consider habitual deviation from NICE guidance (or some similar valid source) as possible experimentation, unless based on sound judgement applied to particular cases.
9. Persuasion to toe the corporate line may require the application of rewards or sanctions.
10. Clinical governance can only change practice if extra resources are applied or existing resources are redirected.
11. Where clinical governance provokes an ethical conflict independent mediation should be attempted before any sanctions are applied.
12. Fusion, common alignment and enhancement of existing quality and performance mechanisms will achieve the objectives of clinical governance most efficiently.
13. Synergy will be gained by working with others with overlapping goals.
14. Patients should be talked through all the appropriate and relevant options, even those immediately unavailable on the NHS.

Table 10.2 Clinical governance – principles for remedying bad practice

1. Most cases of bad practice will be identified by repeated aberrant behaviour, either in one aspect of practice or over several areas of practice.
2. Some training and experience in the law, conflict resolution, medical jurisprudence or ethics are minimum requirements for those obliged to judge alleged malpractice and poor performance.
3. Civil and criminal law are established and appropriate remedies in some cases of malpractice where grievance is significant and a careless individual is most likely at fault.
4. Systems failures require managerial solutions.
5. Where education is deficient, postgraduate deans should be engaged to determine where deficiencies lie, how they might be addressed and to see that the resulting personal development plan is completed and evaluated.
6. Procedures employed to investigate alleged malpractice must be sensitive to physical, mental and social health issues affecting the doctor.
7. Investigation of alleged malpractice must be positive and sympathetic.
8. Those investigating and managing alleged bad practice must resist punitive tendencies.
9. Above all else, the purpose of all endeavours to address malpractice is to prevent future lapses in care.
10. Skilled mediation may be appropriate in simple mishaps and misunderstandings.
11. Local performance committees and the like must secure undertakings from the relevant agencies to guarantee access to the potentially necessary remedial resources before they commence proceedings.

References

Burrows JW (1982). *Charles Darwin: The Origin of Species*. London: Penguin

Connell G (1991). Soren Kierkegaard. In Lachs J, Hassell M (eds) *The Giants of Philosophy. (Audio)*. Nashville: Knowledge Products

Department of Health (1997). *The New NHS: Modern and Dependable. (Cm 3807)*. London: Department of Health

Department of Health (1998a). *A First Class Service: Quality in the New NHS. (HSC(98)113)*. London: Department of Health

Department of Health (1998b). *Review of Prescribing, Supply & Administration of Medicines: A Report on the Supply and Administration of Medicines under Group Protocols*. London: Department of Health

Department of Health (1999a). *Supporting Doctors, Protecting Patients: A Consultation Paper on Preventing, Recognising and Dealing with Poor Performance of Doctors in the NHS in England – Executive Summary.* London: Department of Health

Department of Health (1999b). *Supporting Doctors, Protecting Patients: A Consultation Paper on Preventing, Recognising and Dealing with Poor Performance of Doctors in the NHS in England.* London: Department of Health

Dunbar R (1992). Genes and altruism. In Jones S, Martin R, Pilbeam D (eds). *The Cambridge Encyclopaedia of Human Evolution*. Cambridge: Cambridge University Press

Eddy D (1990). Clinical decision-making: from theory to practice. Practice policies – what are they? *Journal of the American Medical Association* **263**, 877–80

Gaskin JCA (1996). *Thomas Hobbes: Leviathan*. Oxford: Oxford University Press

Glover J (1977). *Causing Death and Saving Lives*. London: Penguin

Hamlyn DW (1980). *Schopenhauer*. Lonodn: Routledge and Kegan Paul

Himmelfarb G (1974). *John Stuart Mill: On Liberty*. London: Penguin

Hollingdale RJ (1990). *Friedrich Nietsche: Beyond Good and Evil*. London: Penguin

Hurwitz B (1998). *Clinical Guidelines and the Law: Negligence, Discretion and Judgement.* Oxon: Radcliffe Medical Press

Institute of Health Services Management (1999). *IHSM Report on Clinical Governance. Clinical Governance: Clinician Heal Thyself?* http://www.ihsm.co.uk./clin_rep.htm

Lee R (1999). Clinical governance and risk management. *The Journal of the MDU* **15**, 9–12

MacDonald D (1993) *The Velvet Claw*. London: BBC Enterprises

Mascaró J (1962). *The Bhagavad Gita*. London: Penguin

National Institute for Clinical Excellence (1999). http://www.nice.org.uk/interact/int_faq.htm

NHS Executive (1999). *Clinical Governance: Quality in the New NHS*. London: Department of Health

Onion CWR (1997). Patient empowerment: help or hindrance. *Economics, Medicines and Health*. Spring, 24–5

Onion CWR (2000). Principles to govern clinical governance. *Journal of Evaluation in Clinical Practice* **6**, 405–412

Onion CWR & Walley T (1998). Clinical guidelines: ways ahead. *Journal of Evaluation in Clinical Practice* **4**, 287–293

Redlich F (1998). *Hitler: Diagnosis of a Destructive Prophet*. New York: Oxford University Press

Russell B (1912). *The Problems of Philosophy*. Oxford: Oxford University Press

Seedhouse D (1988). *Ethics: The Heart of Healthcare*. Chichester: John Wiley & Sons

Singer P (1979). *Practical Ethics*. Cambridge: Cambridge University Press

Sowerby Centre for Health Informatics at Newcastle (1998). *Report on the Results of PRODIGY Phase Two.* Newcastle-upon-Tyne: University of Newcastle-upon-Tyne

Tredennik H & Tarrant H (1993). *Plato: the Last Days of Socrates*. London: Penguin

Warnock M (1972). *The Philosophy of Sartre*. London: Hutchinson

Wooton D (1993). *John Locke: Political Writings*. London: Penguin

Chapter 11

Clinical governance: developing organisational capability

Aidan Halligan, Susanna Nicholls and Steve O'Neill

Development of quality

For most of its first 40 years the NHS worked with an implicit notion of quality, building on the philosophy that the provision of well-trained staff, good facilities and equipment was synonymous with high standards.

Quality initiatives have been developed over the years, but frequently they have failed to achieve meaningful improvement apparent either to the health service or to patients.

During the 1980s managers and policy makers in many parts of the public sector, including healthcare, tried to apply the approaches of total quality management and continuous quality improvement which were originally developed in Japanese industry (Juran 1964; Deming 1986). At that time they did not gain widespread acceptance, perhaps because they were viewed as too management-driven with no clearly identified role for clinical staff.

During the 1990s, following the Quality of Medical Care initiative, medical and clinical audit encouraged a more systematic approach. However, these initiatives were criticised as being professionally dominated, and frequently failing to close the 'action' loop which moves recommendations through agreement into practice.

The philosophy of evidence-based medicine which started in North America (Evidence-based Medicine Working Group 1992) rapidly became international in its scope and was embraced by the health service in Britain. The resultant more effective and consistent transfer of the lessons of research into routine practice has been carried forward as a core component of clinical governance, although the barriers still to be overcome remain formidable.

Professional attitudes and behaviour, access to valid and appropriate information, an effective infrastructure of information technology, and training in the skills of critical appraisal and clinical practice guideline use are just some of the developmental challenges.

Clinical governance therefore came at the end of a decade in which quality had been more explicitly addressed than ever before. It offered a means to integrate previously rather disparate and fragmented approaches to quality improvement – but there was another driver for change.

The series of high profile failures in standards of NHS care in Britain over the last five years – paediatric cardiac surgery at United Bristol Hospital Trust, cervical screening at Kent and Canterbury Hospitals Trust, the Harold Shipman scandal, organ retention issues focused on Alder Hey and others caused deep public and professional concern and threatened to undermine confidence in the NHS. Unwittingly, these events seem to have fulfilled a key criterion in the classic analysis of Kotter (1995) of what does achieve successful change in organisations – the need to establish a sense of urgency (Kotter 1995).

Shortly after coming to office in the late 1990s the new government imposed on every local NHS organisation a statutory duty of quality (Department of Health 1997) and *A First Class Service: Quality in the New NHS* (Donaldson 1998) introduced the concept of clinical governance. This paper promised national service frameworks for key diseases and conditions, a National Institute for Clinical Excellence to set standards and a Commission for Health Improvement to monitor them. Quality was to become, 'a prevailing purpose rather than a desirable accessory.'

Learning from experience in the development of quality

In the context of developing skills to improve organisational learning, and so developing capacity for quality improvement, Chief Medical Officer Professor Liam Donaldson recently chaired an expert group on learning from adverse events in the NHS. Its report, *An Organisation with a Memory* (Department of Health 2000) recognises that 'the great majority of NHS care is of a very high standard'. However, it says the 'devastating consequences' of serious failures for patients, staff and public confidence are made worse because 'such failures often have a familiar ring'. They display 'strong similarities to incidents which have occurred before and in some cases almost exactly replicate them'.

The expert group examined the degree to which the NHS has the capacity to learn from serious failures and looked at evidence of improved practice elsewhere for better understanding of the problems faced by the health service.

Industry and aviation have both demonstrated that the creation of 'safety cultures' – an environment where open reporting and system analysis are encouraged – has a positive impact on performance and safety. In contrast, a 'blame culture' – where attention and blame are focused on the individual rather than on the underlying systems – encourages people to ignore and disguise errors for fear of retribution.

Unfortunately 'the culture of the NHS still errs too much towards the latter' and there is a marked failure to build in learning from experience – to practise 'active learning'.

An Organisation with a Memory clearly shows (by reference to evidence and examples) the value of the systematic recording of 'near misses' as well as 'adverse events'. These incidents can then become learning tools. Currently the NHS has 'no standardised reporting system – nor in fact, a standard definition of what should be reported'.

The Chief Medical Officer has called for a 'fundamental rethinking' of the way the NHS deals with adverse events. There are four key recommendations:

1. Consistent methods for reporting and analysis when things go wrong.
2. A more open culture, in which errors or service failures can be reported and discussed.
3. Mechanisms for ensuring that, where lessons are identified, the necessary changes are made.
4. A much wider appreciation of the importance of systems that underpin processes and hence outcomes.

Work is currently taking place to implement the necessary support structures to implement the recommendations of *An Organisation with a Memory*. The NHS plan (Secretary of State for Health 2000) proposes a mandatory reporting scheme for adverse healthcare incidents which will capitalise on the work begun by the expert group that produced *An Organisation with a Memory*. A single database for 'analysing and sharing the lessons from incidents and near misses' should be available from the end of 2001.

The cost of poor healthcare quality

For patients

A pilot study of inpatients in London found 10 per cent of all inpatient episodes led to harmful adverse events. The direct cost of additional days in hospital was £250,000 for 1,011 admissions. Broad extrapolation would suggest there are 850,000 admissions leading to harmful events in the NHS each year, costing up to £2bn in additional bed days.

The UK's national confidential inquiries suggest 1,150 suicides a year occur among people who have had some contact with health services during the previous 12 months. One hundred and twenty five women a year die during pregnancy or within a year of giving birth. There are almost 8,000 still births and infant deaths per year. And 20,000 people die within 30 days of surgery.

An Organisation with a Memory acknowledges that we still have an incomplete picture of the scale of service failures in the NHS. These figures 'must be regarded as a serious underestimate of the size of the problem' – in particular because there are no shared reporting systems for adverse incidents in primary care.

For staff

Albert Wu (2000) coined the term the 'second victim' to describe the impact on individual members of staff of medical error. This term encapsulates the idea that the individual who is involved in an error or adverse event is largely left to handle the fall-out alone.

> You feel singled out and exposed – seized by the instinct to see if anyone has noticed. You agonise about what to do, whether to tell anyone, what to say ... reassurance from colleagues is often grudging or qualified ... the kind of unconditional sympathy and support that are really needed are rarely forthcoming ... .

Adverse healthcare events have a wider impact too, on clinical teams and colleagues. There is unease and disquiet all round when accidents happen – and the NHS has not yet learned to understand how to analyse and organise systems so that they support staff and protect patients. We still 'pass blame around until the music stops and someone has to face it' (Crossley 2000).

Recent policies on whistleblowing are designed to support those who are concerned about abuse or malpractice. Managed appropriately this in turn supports a culture that is open and allows dialogue rather than one characterised by secrecy and blame.

In litigation

In England at any one time there are some 20,000 cases pending against NHS trusts and some 5,000 new claims a year. The exact cost of these claims is difficult to establish. The House of Commons public accounts committee said £79m was paid out in 1997–1998, while the NHS Litigation Authority's 1999 report and accounts showed its future liabilities for major claims as £312m. Less than a year later, the Auditor General calculated that the total outstanding liability of the NHS was £2.8bn (although this figure has been criticised for including claims that will never generate a payout).

Litigation, however, is only the tip of the risk management cost-iceberg. It is estimated that only one case in ten reaches the courts. The hidden costs of the 90 per cent of cases that do not make it to court are largely unknown, but undoubtedly enormous.

Clinical governance – the structure is in place

The government has established a framework to support the delivery of local clinical governance built on:

1. Standard setting (National Institute for Clinical Excellence, National Service Frameworks).
2. Assuring quality in individual practice (NHS performance procedures, annual appraisal, continuous professional development, revalidation).
3. Scrutiny (Commission for Health Improvement).
4. Learning mechanisms (adverse incident reporting, continuing professional development as well as cross service initiatives through the Modernisation Agency).
5. Patient empowerment (new ways of capturing the patient experience, new representative bodies, involvement in service improvement and development initiatives).

6. Underpinning strategies (information and information technology, research and development, education and training).

But what does the structure look like?

Clinical governance has been defined as 'a framework through which NHS organisations are accountable for continually improving the quality of their services and safeguarding high standards of care by creating an environment in which excellence in clinical care will flourish' (Scally & Donaldson 1998).

Clinical governance is a whole system approach to the delivery of safe, accountable, quality-assured healthcare. It integrates technical issues such as performance monitoring and audit with an understanding of the cultural factors that shape the way in which organisations and people operate and services are delivered.

Clinical governance means seeing services 'through the patient's eyes'; it means valuing the talents, skills and contributions of all the healthcare professionals who contribute to care, creating well-led, empowered teams and understanding that none of us can adequately perform our function, or create the quality service our patients deserve, alone.

Moss *et al.* (1988) suggets that a patient with a probable diagnosis of lung cancer will have contact with approximately 20 hospital professionals including a consultant. While it is the consultant who usually discusses the diagnosis and the treatment opions, 'the decisions about care cannot be made without the contributions from the 19 others'.

The implementation of clinical governance is dependent upon a culture where we work effectively in teams so that together we can produce a top quality service.

Effective teamwork

Effective teamwork is knowing that the conversation your patient had with the porter when he was wheeled off for his barium enema is what he remembered of his hospital visit and what he repeated to his wife that evening. It is knowing that when the staff nurse sorted out a problem with a pension book left at home it solved a problem that was bigger for the patient than the problem solved when his pleural effusion was tapped.

Catalysing cultural change

The Clinical Governance Support Team – practical support to implement clinical governance

The NHS Clinical Governance Support Team (CGST) has been established to support the implementation of clinical governance across the NHS. The Team offers a series of unique programmes to support NHS organisations, their leaders and their teams as they work to create organisational capacity for continuous quality improvement and the delivery of safe and high quality care.

Catalysing the necessary cultural shift

The relationship between quality improvement and organisational culture has been understood in business and industry for many years. The need to 'change the way we do things around here' in order to achieve continuous quality improvement was recognised as the government set out its vision for quality healthcare in 1997:

> ... achieving meaningful and sustainable quality improvements in the NHS requires a fundamental shift in culture, to focus effort where it is needed and to enable and empower those who work in the NHS to improve quality locally.
>
> (Department of Health 1997)

As we work to implement improving quality in NHS organisations the features of the enlightened culture that will support quality development become clear:

1. Patients are central – nothing about me, without me.
2. Staff are valued – an asset in which to invest, not a cost to save.
3. There is active learning – learning lessons from experience.
4. Questions are asked in the spirit of open learning and shared progress.

The CGST has developed a range of challenging clinical governance development programmes for NHS staff which help delegate teams to catalyse cultural change in their host organisations. The learning programmes provide the tools, resources and project management support to facilitate the development and implementation of clinical governance at a local level.

The Clinical Development Programme (CDP) consists of five learning days over a nine-month period. Some 250 organisations from across the NHS have committed multidisciplinary teams of delegates to its task-based work programme.

> The Clinical Governance Support Team invites NHS Chief Executives and boards to:
>
> 'send us staff who will be missed, not staff who can be spared'

Delegate teams attend a series of five, task-orientated workshops (learning days) over a period of nine months. During this time, in their sponsoring organisations, delegates lead project teams as they design and deliver multiple quality improvement initiatives.

The CGST reinforces top-down support and championship for delegate teams when it visits health organisations and meets with members of their boards. A visit helps boards understand exactly what staff have already achieved in the workplace and it helps set these achievements in the context of the wider organisation so that strategies for spread can be considered. The visit facilitates board teams as they develop an organisational culture that supports whole system, multilevel improvement initiatives and healthcare professionals who 'learn as they do'.

> 'The only way to achieve lasting organisational change is project by project, and there is no other way.'

Delegate teams on the programme follow the RAID (Review, Agree, Implement, Demonstrate) model (Figure 11.1) to initiate a project culture within their organisation.

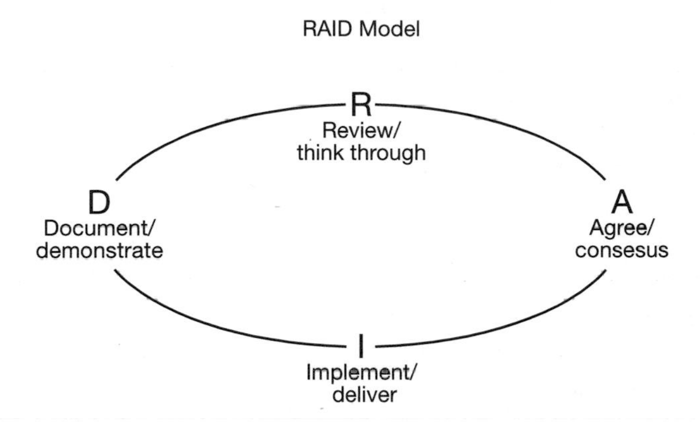

Figure 11.1 RAID model developed by National Clinical Governance Support Team

Bridging the knowing–doing gap

The review process – where are we now? And where are we going?

The review part of the process involves a large-scale review of current service – gathering staff and patient views, inspecting and analysing current practice, collecting evidence about current known best practice, etc. The process encourages the examination of traditionally accepted 'unwritten rules' and beliefs. It gives a licence to staff to express their passion in a disciplined and effective manner – it allows them to 'believe again' and validates them as individuals who deserve appropriate recognition and value.

A group of 40 senior healthcare professionals was recently asked to list the 'unwritten rules' by which we work in the NHS. Their list is worth reproducing in full (Figure 11.2).

Agreement – winning hearts and minds

The agreement phase involves flagging up the hard route that lies ahead if improvement changes are to be initiated. It ensures that all healthcare alliances and partners have been involved and are contributing to the delivery of a 'joined-up' vision. This phase is about winning hearts and minds (Figure 11.3).

Implementation and demonstration

The implementation phase capitalises on the enthusiasm previously generated. Healthcare professionals are keen to measure, to know and to prove that they are making an important difference for patients. They move naturally into the demonstration phase where improvement activities are reflected in hard data which is then used to manage future development (Figure 11.4).

Clinical governance support team supports

The prospectus warns that the Programme is demanding – and delegates arrive with a number of common anxieties (Figure 11.5).

Each team of delegates works with a CGST project manager who makes regular on-site visits. Delegates are helped to identify existing resources within their organisation, and to secure more if necessary; training, research and educational materials are made available; there is telephone and electronic access to the team and to project managers for advice and individual support.

Clinical governance development programme – the learning days

Learning day 1

The first learning day is in part designed to help delegates understand themselves and each other, to recognise the differences between people and to begin to understand what such differences can contribute. Delegates identify some of the real-life problems (involving people, processes and systems) encountered in the face of change, and explore different methods of approaching them.

Learning day 2

The second learning day concentrates on the components of successful change – culture, technique and strategy. Delegates work out how to plan a comprehensive review of the area in which they intend to undertake a programme of improvement and explore a range of tools to assist as they assess baseline performance and gather patient and staff views. Time is spent considering the mechanism of the review exercise as an important means of engaging and involving staff and of creating awareness and insight.

Meetings are the best way to get people together
We know best
Meetings constitute activity
My own work has no effect on other areas of the NHS
Anonymity confers mutual protection
We all need a siege mentality
It's OK to winge but not to complain officially
We all have to be super-human
Clinicians don't need managers
Only someone of my profession understands my problem
Administrators are managers
Pass 'problems' up the line
What are you going to do about it?
Unless there is a protocol for it, it's not happening
Filing in the form makes it happen.
You have to be as honest as possible without saying anything out of line
The more senior you are the more you know!
Doctors know better than nurses
You have to work as long as the person who works longest
You have to do things cheaply
I don't have to do it – someone else will
Deadlines are made to be missed
You can't have a cup of tea without making one for everyone
Only do something if there is money in it
Doctors don't understand managers and vice versa
Don't admit to mistakes
Even though we talk about quality we only assess on the quantity.
Doctors know all the answers (i.e., I can't do that, I have to wait for the doctor)
The patients don't like it/won't understand it
But I've always done it this way
People don't change – change is hard.
I haven't got the staff to do that – we need to appoint someone first
We haven't had the right training to do that
There are no rewards for doing well
Everyone understands the jargon
It is wrong to seek answers/consult others
It is wrong to be wrong ...
... and it is wrong to admit to being wrong.
Change costs money and means more stress.
Some people are more valuable than others ...
... and some people's time is more valuable than others
We know best
Don't fix it if it's not bust
There is a pressure to introduce change for change's sake
I'm the only one who cares
Only women can do touchy/feely (nurses)
Consultant time is more important than anyone else's
Doctors' time is more valuable than nurses'
We can't make GPs change because they're independent contractors
Everything is changing all the time
The past was much better

Figure 11.2 Unwritten rules in the NHS

The Challenge:

- Winning hearts and minds – we've tried before ... nothing ever changes
- Isolated pockets of good practice
- No comprehensive service-wide agreed strategy
- Poor communication between professionals and organisations necessary to deliver complete care package
- Staff felt demotivated and demoralised

The Solution:

- Workshops were held with the Board and with staff from all disciplines and departments across Mental Health and Social Services
- Users and their carers were invited to their own workshops
- Individual face to face meetings were held with professionals from all disciplines and all services to obtain a broad view of the service and a vision for the future

Large representation from the Mental Health economy in Harrow was sought at a whole-systems meeting held to develop a vision for excellence in mental healthcare.
The following people made a commitment to a joint vision and to applying new ways of working:

Psychologists
Physiotherapists
Social workers
Counsellors
Administration staff
Domestic staff
Secretaries
Voluntary sector organisations
Special needs professionals
Primary care professionals
Psychiatrists
Educators
Nurses
Porters
CHC staff
LA staff
Housing staff
GPs
Health authority staff

Figure 11.3 Gaining agreement and sharing a vision in mental health: Delegates on the Clinical Development Programme

Learning day 3

Typically on the third learning day delegates report that their work on the review process has been illuminating 'the more talking we did to people about the programme the more help we elicited' ... 'listening to people who work in the service is one of the best ways of defining the issues'. The third day of the programme concentrates on effectively communicating the results and recommendations of the review, and building the infrastructure necessary to implement a programme of improvement change.

By now delegates have identified which of their workplace projects will produce early benefits. They review the non-linear relationship between effort and results using the Pareto method (Juran 1974) and work out how early benefits can be used to speed the process of change.

24 project teams:

Improving the efficiency of outpatient clinics
- To reduce waiting times
- To minimise staff frustrations
- To improve efficiency of clinic

Critical case analysis – gynaecology
- To address risk management in gynaecology

Rest and recuperation for staff
- To create a rest area where staff may relax and take meal breaks

Standards, use and storage of medical records
- To improve current standards of maternity note keeping

Access to library facilities
- To maximise opportunities for access to library facilities for all staff

Review of junior doctors' hours
- To create better working conditions for Juniors

Review of antenatal ward attenders
- To ensure that antenatal attenders are investigated, reviewed and discharged home as appropriate and without delay

Confidentiality in antenatal clinic
- To ensure that confidentiality is respected at all times

Transfer to community midwife care
- To improve communication between hospital and community carers at discharge interface
- To minimise communication errors and therefore risks

Learning bases for staff
- To offer midwives the stability and security of a ward base while they are working outside the hospital
- To improve educational and learning experiences for staff

24 hour, multidisciplinary team working
- To encourage and enable all staff to adopt a wider role in the provision of a 24-hour service for patients and families

Bed making on the Maternity Unit
- To reduce the amount of time spent making beds

Review of facilities offered by Early Pregnancy Assessment Unit
- To improve the facilities for women and families attending the unit
- To improve the working environment for staff working in the unit

Information for women and teenagers
- To increase opportunities for women and teenagers to access information about women's health issues

Maintaining a clean and safe environment on gynaecology wards
- To ensure that all equipment is working, clean and safe
- To ensure that all clinical areas are clean and safe

Clerical support within the directorate
- To improve the service to patients by providing adequate clerical support for nurses and midwives
- To review and develop the role of the ward clerk

cont'd.

Figure 11.4 'Let's Make It Better ...' a delegate team working in obstetrics & gynaecology

Review of volunteer services
- To maximise the contribution made to the care of women and their families by volunteers and the voluntary services

To actively seek and respond to users' views
- To seek users views and use them to shape and monitor services

Facilities for inpatients
- To improve the facilities for long stay and short stay patients

To maintain effective communication
- To ensure that all staff are kept informed and involved

Shift patterns
- To review shift patterns to seek improvement in continuity of care for patients
- To review shift patterns to seek 'family friendly' working patterns

Midwifery led care
- To offer appropriate women the choice of 'low-tech' midwife-led care
- To enhance the role of the midwife
- To improve midwifery skills and development
- To increase job satisfaction

Review of essential equipment in maternity
- To ensure that sufficient equipment is available in all areas to enable healthcare professionals to give best patient care effectively, efficiently and safely

Services are improving for patients and staff

Project teams are 'signed up' to work on the above topics, and many improvement changes have already been made:

- Confidentiality has been improved for patients at reception desks in outpatients
- Users' views are actively being sought – questionnaires, patient diaries, suggestion boxes and users' forums have all been developed and are being used
- A partial shift system has been introduced for junior doctors
- A 'quiet room' has been provided in the Antenatal Clinic
- Volunteers have been integrated into the multidisciplinary team in gynaecology
- There is a weekly bulletin which keeps all staff in the directorate informed and involved in developments
- 50 new pillows have been bought
- New toys have been bought for the Antenatal Clinic waiting room
- A washer/dryer machine has been bought for long-stay patients to use (and for patients to wash TEDs)
- Ice-makers have been bought for maternity and gynaecology wards

Figure 11.4 continued

Delegates work together to identify and challenge traditional rules and explore the anxiety that this generates. They explore leadership in teams, project selection, project prioritisation, project management, gaining agreement, and anticipating and dealing with resistance.

Figure 11.5 Poster created by one team of delegates before learning day 1 of the CDP

Learning day 4

On day 4 delegates work on ideas and techniques to analyse current activity and establish baseline performance:

- process mapping – understanding the 'patient journey';
- developing and implementing care pathways – formalising ways of working;
- problem solving and root cause analysis – deal with the cause not the symptom;
- creative thinking – something other than more of the same;
- rapid cycle change – trying it out in the workplace.

There is work around statistical process control and use of root cause analysis and Ishikawa diagrams (Ishikawa 1989) to map causal relationships. Delegates look at the importance of creative thinking and Rapid Cycle Change (Shewart 1931; Deming 1986). Delegates also concentrate on developing a clear understanding of performance measurement – designing measurement parameters for their own improvement initiatives.

After a review of tasks undertaken in action interval four, day 5 emphasises the need for the systematic approach necessary to embed improvement changes within the organisation. Delegates work on complaints management, risk analysis systems, establishing systematic audit with positive feedback action and review loops, critical appraisal skills, personal development plans, and 'skills and training needs' analysis. Lastly they look at spreading innovation within an organisation.

Building organisational capacity for clinical governance

One way of thinking about the implementation of clinical governance is to take an architectural metaphor – a Greek temple built on five foundation stones (Figure 11.6).

These foundation stones are the components of the culture that will support the organisational aspects of successful clinical governance.

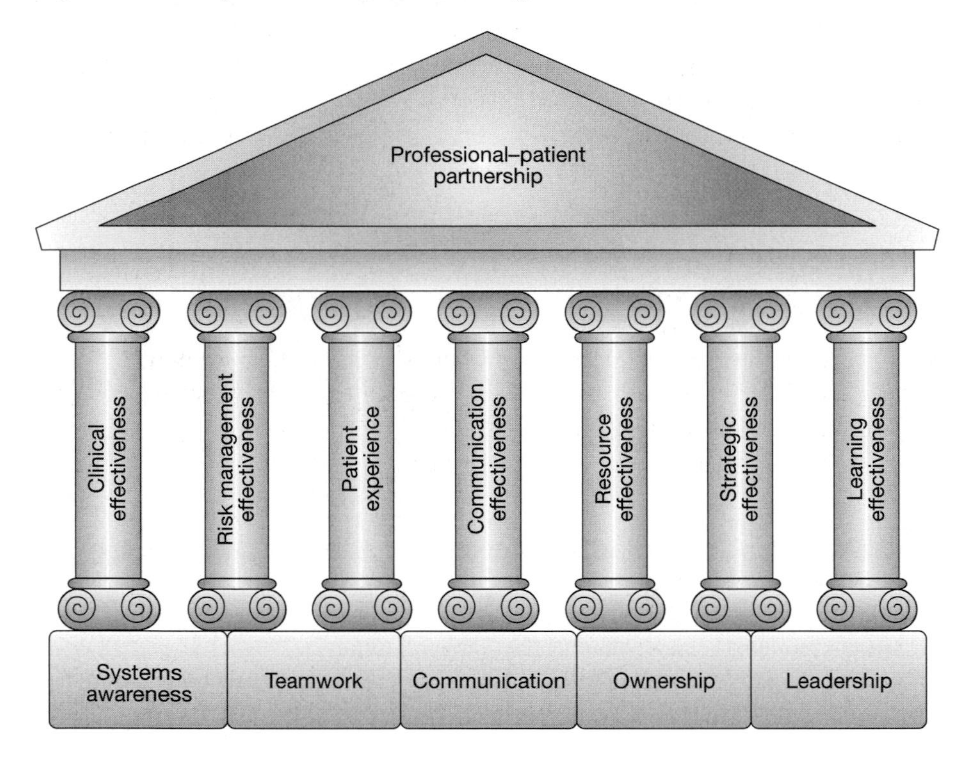

Figure 11.6 Implementation of clinical governance

Systems awareness

An understanding of how systems work and how they can determine not only action but outcome is critical to improving the quality of healthcare. Systems thinking goes beyond 'fault finding' and looks at the structures and relationships involved in an episode of healthcare – at the whole system around a service. Its purpose is therefore diagnostic. It enables an understanding of what works well, what is dysfunctional and what needs improvement.

However, systems awareness is more than understanding that systems are greater than the sum of their parts. It recognises that systems have 'emergent properties'.

A case study – delegate team on clinical governance development programme

Setting: Ambulance Service.

The event:

A paramedic was called to attend an 8-year-old child who had fallen from a tree and fractured his femur. The child was too distressed to use Entonox (inhaled analgesia) and faced a '15 minute carry' to the ambulance. The paramedic gave a dose of Nubain calculated for the child knowing that the protocol in operation forbade administration of Nubain to children under the age of 14. He reported the incident and his actions on return to the station.

What happened next:

1. The Training Officer reviewed the case.
2. The dose correct for age had been given.
3. A report has been sent to the Steering Committee suggesting that paramedics be allowed to administer drugs to children under the age of 14 in accordance with pharmaceutical licensing regulations.
4. The incident was recorded on the Paramedic's Training File.

Key benefits:

1. Improved patient service.
2. Systems become 'patient centred'.
3. Systems to address problems are developed.
4. Staff are encouraged to report incidents.
5. Staff feel supported when events call for sensible, calculated, but new decisions.

As O'Connor and McDermott (1997) argue, a post mortem 'does not discover the secret of life, but death'.

Systems awareness, a recognition of how systems can both support and hamper development, provides the facility to learn and improve.

Leadership

Pam Garside (1998) argues that NHS management has suffered from 'short-termism': 'managers in the NHS in particular are continually forced to focus on immediate solutions to problems and have little opportunity for developing longer term organisational change strategies.'

Clinical governance, and its implementation, give leaders an opportunity to think on a broader scale than they may have done in the past. It is a chance to move from a micro to a macro view, to see the system as a whole, developing tools and techniques for improvement as a result of innovation not reaction.

Staff seeking to introduce improvement also need practical support from senior champions: from managers and boards with the capacity to think strategically and to demonstrate the values they expect their staff to adopt. The behaviour of leaders is important – 'the only effective way to communicate a value is to act in accordance with it and give others the incentive to do the same' (Garside 1998).

Leaders who can make real the vision of a 'desired future state', and who can demonstrate their belief and commitment, will create the momentum to carry change through the inevitable resistance that it will meet.

Clinical governance requires leaders who can:

1. Ascertain all views and incorporate the best.
2. See the future but understand the present.
3. Understand and value differences.
4. Articulate a vision for the team and inspire a commitment to it.
5. Ask questions and not provide the answers.
6. Ask 'wicked questions' which expose longstanding assumptions.
7. Create teams that are not afraid to fail.
8. Be reflective and see the learning in all experiences.

Teamwork

Much of the learning – or rather unlearning of ingrained patterns of behaviour – that flows from systems awareness happens within teams. The health service has been poor at establishing feedback mechanisms and completing action loops. In the past enthusiastic and committed staff have often initiated improvement projects, begun the hard work of implementing change, but then found championship and support from senior levels to be lacking.

Establishing teams that are empowered to make real improvement changes requires a wide perspective on 'teamwork':

1. Providing tangible and visible support at board level and at senior management levels.
2. Building feedback and communication links within and across organisational boundaries.
3. Making links to business and strategic planning mechanisms and processes.

A structured approach to defining the support mechanisms that a team needs to function productively helps those 'at the sharp end' feel that their voice is heard and their contribution acknowledged and valued.

Properly developed, well-led, multidisciplinary teams will become prime levers for change in clinical governance; as teams grow and learn they will be able to both drive and deliver quality improvement initiatives.

An example of teamwork: delegates on the CDP

A team reviewing operating theatre services identified significant problems around lists starting late and then over-running, theatre time and staff time being consequently ill-utilised, patients not being returned to wards when expected, patients having 'to be cancelled', etc. Analysis revealed problems around portering and, following root cause analysis, communication was found to be a system flaw. The porters suggested that if they were connected to the hospital e-mail system things would improve. This proved to be a simple solution to what had seemed a complex problem.

If the porters had not been considered an important and integral part of the team reviewing the service the suggestion for improvement, and its smooth implementation, may never have materialised.

An example of teamwork: delegates on the CDP

One ambulance team working on clinical effectiveness involved a variety of A&E staff from two hospitals – including nurses who ran the minor injuries clinics – in their review team. The team discussed a frustration – paramedics were empowered to diagnose a suspected myocardial infarction and direct the patient appropriately to the Coronary Care Unit. However, patients with obvious, simple, minor injury frequently had to be driven past the nurse-led minor injuries clinic at one hospital to the A&E department at another. It did not take long to sort out the obvious inefficiency, change guidelines, and thereby validate professionalism and recognise appropriate competence across the healthcare team.

Without the right to redesign systems, frontline staff – who have a clear understanding of systems and their flaws – will continue to experience frustration and inefficiency. Patients, staff and organisations lose out if there is ineffective teamworking.

Communication

Communication is not simply passing information from those who have it to those who need it. Effective communication is also about listening. Effective communication helps create a wider awareness – to include the perspectives of all those involved in the process of healthcare.

Ownership

Ownership is about getting the real participation of all of those involved in a service. A team that values the diversity and encourages the input of all its members will collect the best ideas and create the most imaginative solutions. The best ideas often come from those who have never before been asked.

An example of staff taking ownership of their service, and of their patient's problem:

PT, unaware of her pregnancy, was exposed to chemicals known to be teratogenic. She rang her Community Midwife who (using direct referral system) arranged an urgent hospital appointment and ultrasound scan.

On arrival the patient was impressed that the ultrasonographer:

1. Knew all about the history – she didn't have to repeat herself.
2. Had researched the chemical involved and knew the risks.
3. Explained the risks to her as she scanned specifically to look for possible effects.

During the same hospital appointment the patient was seen by an obstetrician who also knew the history, had the ultrasonographer's report, and could provide further reassurance.

In this case then there was effective communication – between patient and professional, between professionals, and between community and hospital.

There were systems in place to allow an early and appropriate response to an expressed anxiety (direct midwifery referral, co-ordinated open clinic system to allow scan, report and consultation at same visit). Staff had access to the necessary information and the information technology systems to access it where and when appropriate.

Each professional took ownership of their part in this patient's problem and they liaised effectively and efficiently – they worked together as a team.

The 'pillars' of clinical governance

Clinical effectiveness

Clinical effectiveness is about making sure that treatment and care are being informed and driven by evidence of effectiveness and a systematic assessment of health outcomes.

Clinical governance requires teams and organisations to demonstrate their clinical effectiveness. This means agreeing appropriate clinical indicators, measuring around them and then benchmarking against best practice. Drivers for clinical effectiveness include the National Service Frameworks, Royal College and local guidelines, work from NICE, the Audit Commission and SIGN, as well as robust and meaningful interpretation of patient experience.

Increasing the knowledge base about what is effective is vital and it is important to create the mechanisms and enhance skills of staff so that clinical practice can be shaped in the light of best evidence and available knowledge.

Risk management effectiveness

Risk management can be defined as the identification, evaluation and control of potential adverse outcomes that compromise the delivery of appropriate care to patients.

It is not sufficient simply to record untoward incidents, complaints and claims. A wider, more systematic approach is required to review systems and seek out potential risks. We need to learn how best to seek safety information actively, and how to analyse it properly in order to inform developments that will minimise risk and eliminate hazards to patient care and well-being.

Patient experience

The experience of the patient is crucial to governance and to achieving a balance of power between professionals and those receiving care. Sometimes the complexity of the organisations in which we all work allow the patient to slip out of focus in quality improvement initiatives. Enabling and facilitating patient and carer involvement at all stages of development work ensure that they remain central. There are now many established mechanisms for collecting patient experience information, and we are learning new ways of involving them in quality development work. As we get better at clinical governance we will improve our ability to involve patients and carers successfully and meaningfully.

Communication effectiveness

Communication is one of the most important processes in any organisation. It has major effects on the performance and success of individuals, teams and the organisation itself. Good communication builds productive relationships between staff and patients. Effective communication involves sharing information, reaching a common understanding and listening as well as talking.

Communication needs to be actively managed to make clinical governance a reality.

When members of a clinical team develop the habit and systems of effective communication they become clear about what matters to individuals – patients and staff – and therefore quickly see how best to shape the process of healthcare.

Project work by ambulance trust delegates on the CDP

How it was:

1. Communication system was by radio.
2. Messages about patients in transit were relayed from the Ambulance Crew via Central Control to Hospital.
3. Messages sometimes failed to reach the Hospital.
4. Messages sometimes were muddled – 'it was Chinese whispers'.

How it is now:

1. Crews have mobile telephones.
2. They liaise directly with the admitting hospital.

The benefits:

1. No more mixed or lost messages.
2. Ambulance crews can receive clinical advice direct from staff in A&E.
3. A&E staff can help determine best receiving hospital for patients.
4. A&E staff are always aware of patients en route and can manage resources accordingly.

Resource effectiveness

As healthcare technologies continue to develop and people live longer there will be increasing pressure on healthcare resources. Yet the resources available for healthcare are finite and it is essential to ensure that they are used effectively.

Often when healthcare professionals express their concerns about implementing clinical governance they talk about a lack of resources and a lack of funding. Yet delivering high-quality healthcare requires far more than money. It requires the effective utilisation of people, time, equipment, buildings, information technology and knowledge. Health-care quality has been defined as 'doing the right thing, for the right person at the right time and getting it right first time, every time' (Donaldson 1998). Developing the culture that will support and enable staff to deliver excellence will not cost money, only effort.

Crosby (1980) argues that 'quality is free' because its development frees funds. He identifies three ways in which this can happen:

1. Failure costs – accrued when things go wrong. For example:

- Increased lengths of hospital stay.
- Unplanned returns to the operating theatre.
- Preventable re-admissions to hospital.
- Costs of treating hospital-acquired infection and its consequences.
- Unnecessary returns for outpatient appointments.
- Non-value-adding on-going visits by primary healthcare teams.
- Consumables being date expired due to poor rotation of held stock.
- Equipment becoming unusable due to lack of maintenance.

2. Prevention costs

Preventing waste of resources involves ensuring that there are mechanisms in place that increase the chances of getting things right first time, every time. Such processes include identifying and learning from occasions when things go wrong and putting in place systems that prevent the same thing happening again.

3. Appraisal costs

Appraisal costs can be defined as the costs of measuring quality and evaluating the care patients receive and the benefit they experience in terms of clinical outcome. Although establishing measurement processes to enable benchmarking, quality improvement definition, risk management, audits etc. will engender costs, considerable improvement in the effective use of resources will result.

Clinical governance demands of us all that we work within clinical teams and in learning organisations to become 'strategic thinkers' not 'strategic planners'.

You don't always need more money ... improving patient care – a delegate team working on the CDP

Working smarter ...

1. Ambulance crews carry sealed drug boxes. Whenever the seal is broken the box has to be returned to the nearest acute hospital for replacement.
2. An audit across two stations revealed that some 82 drug boxes had been replaced during a two-month period when the only drug to be used was salbutamol nebule.
3. The ambulance trust is charged a few pence for the nebule, and £4 for replacing and re-sealing the drug box.
4. They projected that the two stations could save £1,968 p.a. by keeping salbutamol in a locked cabinet in the ambulance, the drug box, and have gained agreement to implement this change across the 19 stations of the trust.

And with the money they save ...

1. Currently they have no means of diagnosing hypoglycaemia – they assume it if the patient is unconscious, confused or unmanageable with grounds for suspicion – and treat with intravenous or intramuscular glucagon.
2. They plan to buy each crew a glucometer and associated equipment (stix, lance sets, etc.) so they can improve diagnosis and treatment of hypoglycaemia.

Strategic effectiveness

This 'pillar' is a key integrating component in the architecture of clinical governance. For strategy to be effective it must link an organisation's values, aspirations and future with its operational capacities and capabilities. There needs to be consistency in four key areas:

1. Purpose – what are we here for?
2. Values – what do we believe in?
3. Strategy – where are we going and how?
4. Behaviour – what standards and levels of competence do we want to work to?

Organisational leadership has a key role to play in creating this alignment. Clinical governance requires that all stakeholders in the delivery of healthcare are heard and that, as strategy and 'the way forward' is planned, all stakeholders are involved. Management of a healthcare organisation involves the co-ordination of many technical concerns – IT, healthcare technology, the management of assets and financial control. The hallmark of strategic effectiveness is the union of all these elements so that they provide a cohesive means by which to achieve a shared vision.

Learning effectiveness

As we begin to challenge the unwritten rules and the silent assumptions that for too long have hidebound the NHS, we will develop an open culture of learning which will enable the clear and fearless definition of quality and support the design of systems and route to achieve it. There will be unlearning, as well as learning.

The work of Bob Garratt (1997) suggests that an organisation can only become effective and efficient if there is continuous learning between the leaders who direct the organisation, the staff who work in it and the patients or users of the service.

Organisations are typically constrained in the way they solve problems and the way they act by what are often 'unwritten rules'. Such rules create inertia within the system and ingrained, patterned behaviour inhibits change.

Challenging or altering these rules is one of the key steps in the successful leadership of change. Staff need to be empowered to ask 'difficult questions' of themselves, each other and their organisation. When staff and patients are enabled to take a questioning and challenging approach to 'the way things are done around here' the culture becomes open and questioning, and supportive of improvement change. As we start to ask the difficult questions, to make the undiscussable discussable, we sow the seeds for successful clinical governance.

Learning will only take place if it can be nurtured and encouraged in an organisation where people feel empowered to make change, to take measured risks, to be creative in innovation and promoting best practice. Individuals require a supportive environment to learn, change behaviour and sustain improvement change.

Supportive approaches to learning from experience, appraisal, continuous professional development, incident reporting and analysis are all part of the fabric of an organisation that can learn effectively.

The projects and programmes that delegates lead within their organisations provide a wealth of learning and examples of best practice. The CGST is committed to sharing this through its website (www.cgsupport.org), publishing and presentations. The improvement work that is being completed under the auspices of the Clinical Governance Support Team and the work of the team itself are contributing to the evidence base and to the literature on successfully managing organisational change.

Some further examples of working models/case studies follow.

Case study from delegates on the Clinical Governance Development Programme

South Manchester Primary Care NHS Trust & South Manchester University Hospitals NHS Trust

Clinical area: care of diabetic patients

The challenge:

1. Poor communication between primary and secondary care professionals.
2. Information occasionally lost at primary and secondary interface.
3. Professionals had inadequate access to advice and guidance.
4. Healthcare professionals in Nursing Homes and Teams for Care of the Elderly felt isolated.
5. Patients had inadequate access to advice.
6. 'Patients had to fit into the existing service' – it was not patient-centred.

The approach:

A multidisciplinary project steering team – professionals from primary and secondary care – is leading 16 project teams working on, for example:

1. Establishing a Community Team including dieticians, podiatrists, diabetic specialist nurses and therapists to provide information and advice for professionals.
2. Involving patients in re-shaping services.
3. Capacity building in primary care – e.g. glucose meters for District Nurses.
4. Establishing an adolescent clinic.
5. Creating a multidisciplinary education programme.
6. Developing a structured programme of diabetic care.
7. Developing a patient-held record.
8. Creating a diabetes services map.

The benefits:

1. Improved communication between primary and secondary care.
2. A wide primary healthcare team is now involved in service planning.
3. Professionals working in Nursing Homes and Elderly Care Teams are now involved in service planning.
4. There will be improved access to information for professionals caring for patients at home.
5. Multi-professional teamwork and new education programmes have enabled individuals to improve skill and knowledge bases.

Case study from delegates on the Clinical Governance Development Programme

The Royal Bournemouth and Christchurch Hospitals NHS Trust

Clinical area: stroke care

The problem:

1. Two sites with different processes of care.
2. Concern about a perceived poorer standard of care for outlying patients.
3. Communication between the two units was poor.
4. Inconsistency of approach between the two units.
5. Reporting delays meant standards for brain scanning were not being met.
6. Patient information was inconsistent in content.
7. Some staff were 'parochial' with limited commitment to a broad view of the service.
8. Communication to patients and carers about care plans, diagnosis, etc. was 'patchy'.
9. There was an inconsistency of approach to rehabilitation of patients
10. Staff felt that there was limited education and little opportunity for professional and personal development.

The solution:

1. Multidisciplinary project teams have been established.
2. An integrated care pathway has been planned for all stroke patients.
3. A wide range of disciplines and therapists is now involved in planning and delivering care.
4. A workshop has been developed to review the interface between primary and secondary care.
5. An inter-professional educational rolling programme has been agreed.
6. Patient information will be reviewed with the help of patients and carers.

The benefits:

1. An equitable and improved standard of care for all stroke patients.
2. Improved and relevant information for patients and carers.
3. Communication between professionals has been improved.
4. Staff are involved in educational and training programmes and are enhancing skills.
5. A review of data collection has revealed unnecessary duplication and will enable increased efficiency of documentation.

The future

The Modernisation Agency – of which the CGST is a part from April 2001 – will have an active knowledge management strategy to help embed continuous quality improvement. The CGST is also working with other national partners in clinical governance policy and practice to define the best ways to use measurement and assessment to support the implementation of clinical governance. The work of the CGST is being formally evaluated in order to inform future development further.

References

Crosby PB (1980). *Quality is Free.* New York: Penguin

Crossley T (2000). Doctors and nurses should monitor each other's performance. *British Medical Journal* **320**, 1070–1071

Deming WE (1986). *Out of the Crisis.* Cambridge: Cambridge University Press

Department of Health (1997). *The New NHS: Modern, Dependable.* London: The Stationery Office

Department of Health (2000). *An Organisation with a Memory: Report of an Expert Group on Learning from Adverse Events in the NHS.* London: The Stationery Office

Donaldson LJ (1998). *A First Class Service: Quality in the New NHS.* London: Department of Health

Evidence-based Medicine Working Group (1992). Evidence-based medicine: a new approach to teaching the practice of medicine. *Journal of the American Medical Association* **268**, 2420–2425

Garratt B (1997). *The Fish Rots from the Head. The Crisis in our Boardroom: Developing the Crucial Skills of the Competent Director.* London: Harper Collins

Garside P (1998). Organisational context for quality: lessons from the fields of organisational development and change management. *Quality in Healthcare* **7**, S8–S15

Ishikawa K (1989). *Guide to Quality Control.* New York: Quality Resources

Juran JM (1964). *Managerial Breakthrough.* New York: McGraw-Hill

Juran JM (1974). *Quality Control Handbook,* 3rd edn. New York: McGraw-Hill

Kotter JP (1995). Leading change: why transformation efforts fail. *Harvard Business Review* **59**

Leatherman S & Sutherland K (1998). Evolving quality in the new NHS: policy, process, and pragmatic considerations. *Quality in Healthcare* **7**, S54–S61

Moss F, Garside P, Dawson S (1998). Organisational change: the key to quality improvement. *Quality in Healthcare* **7**, S1–S2

O'Connor J & McDermott I (1997). *The Art of Systems Thinking. Essential Skills for Creativity and Problem Solving*. London: Thorsons

Scally G & Donaldson LJ (1998). Looking forward: clinical governance and the drive for quality improvement in the new NHS in England. *British Medical Journal* **317**, 61–65

Secretary of State for Health (2000). *The NHS Plan: A Plan for Investment, a Plan for Reform.* London: The Stationery Office

Shewhart WA (1931). *Economic Control of Quality of Manufactured Product.* New York: Van Nostrand

Wu AW (2000). Medical error: the second victim. *British Medical Journal* **320**, 726–727

Index